THE
POLITICAL CREATURE
An Evolutionary Reorientation

The Political Creature

AN EVOLUTIONARY
REORIENTATION

Peter Zollinger

GEORGE BRAZILLER NEW YORK

Preface

The beginnings of this book go back to the second World War, which to me, as to many others, meant a deep moral perturbation. I was, at that time, a political correspondent. Being modestly conversant with the sciences and possessing a broader humanistic background, I found myself asking more and more often whether it might not be possible to discover political principles as incontrovertible as those of the physical and biological disciplines. This started me on a survey of those branches of knowledge which I thought might help me find an answer to my problem. It turned out to be a long-drawn-out search, and here, *in nuce*, are its results.

As an attempt to reach valid social and political conclusions on the basis of contemporary science, the enquiry probably represents something new. However, it does not claim to have exhausted the intricate subject nor to offer anything final. If I have succeeded in showing that political civilization is as certainly the outcome of natural evolution as are other phenomena of life and for this reason subject to certain laws of nature, I shall consider myself well rewarded for my efforts. At any rate, in an age which boasts of its scientific spirit (but whose political alchemists have nonetheless driven us to the verge of failure), an essay like the present one should not appear premature.

No formal dedication could convey the depth of gratitude I owe my wife for encouraging and indulging me while the book was in the process of becoming. At three different stages of its development she served as my critic; she bore her share of the burden of proofreading and assisted me with the Index. Thanks are also due to Dr. George Brantl of the publisher's editorial staff for his helpful suggestions and for seeing some merit in my daring.

J.P.Z.

THE
POLITICAL CREATURE

An Evolutionary Reorientation

Contents

Introduction

*The only knowledge of permanent
value is theoretical knowledge.*
RENÉ DUBOS

WHEN Aristotle gave to the human species its first scientific name, *zoon politikon*, he already expressed as well as is possible in two words the fact that man is an animal and yet a very special kind of animal. For he is that extraordinary member of the zoological realm of life whose most typical representatives have contrived the *polis*, the city-state, with its governors and laws, its guilds of craftsmen and merchants, its temples and schools, its sculptors, poets, musicians, architects and philosophers. Aristotle's *zoon politikon*, the "political animal," as it is usually translated, in its truest and fullest meaning therefore denotes nature's civilized and cultured creature. The title of this book should be understood in this sense, because there has never been any kind of civilization except under some sort of political organization.

The task we have set ourselves here, then, is none other than to trace the ways by which a creature that once obeyed only physical and biological laws ascended to a place in the world which allows him, in a measure at least, to make his own laws.

On the other hand, of course, though civilized man seems superficially removed from the general animal kingdom, he has inextricably remained a part of it. As should become evident in the course of this inquiry, exactly his highest achievements, his intellectual life, his social and political institutions, his hopes and

dreams and aspirations, and his pronouncedly historical orientation, are nothing else than the supreme exponential manifestations
of animal nature. I shall therefore in these pages treat man as
neither more nor less than *the animal par excellence,* the one who,
alone among all the rest of the world's creatures, is beginning to
realize the fullest potentialities inherent in the animal principle.
A biology of civilized or political man should lead to a fuller
understanding of the problems which arise when a being transcends the bounds of laws which since the beginning of life automatically took care of the needs of all creatures, and is handed
over to his own responsibilities.

Now, in the philosophical tradition, if rarely in that of professional politicians, the word "politics" has always signified the
manifold activities instituted to safeguard and further men's
freedom of development, to realize more and more of the potentialities still dormant in them. If therefore we follow this tradition,
an evolutionary history of the political animal inevitably also becomes a natural history of human freedom.

Unfortunately, the word "freedom" is one of the more ambigu-
ous in our vocabulary. This is not surprising since, right into the
third decade of the twentieth century, scientists were unanimously
of the opinion that the word had no meaning at all. And if they
graciously condoned its use by esoteric poets and philosophers,
patriotic historians and political orators, as part of the vocabulary
of a self-respecting man of science it remained taboo.

In 1927, however, almost at the snapping of a finger, the scientific attitude changed. What had been the chief taboo of yester-
day overnight became not merely respectable, but a fundamental
concept of science and a basic element of the recognized cosmic
order. It is therefore no longer necessary to apologize for an
attempt to subject to scientific scrutiny the doings of political
man, in whose mental makeup the concept of freedom looms so
large. For if freedom is one of the basic conditions of universal
order, and if it is conceded that politics does not operate in a
cosmic vacuum, it may be assumed that even the laws of political
civilization to some degree must reflect basic universal law.

This view is by no means novel. It was shared by the ancient Chinese sages and the great Greek philosophers. Furthermore, throughout all early Germanic law, of which Anglo-American common law is an offspring, there ran the thought that the striving for social law is but a search for the laws of God, the laws of the universe, that there is but one law, valid throughout the cosmos, and that it will in the end be revealed to man's yearning for truth.[1]

From the present-day viewpoint of science, this "medieval" outlook was astonishingly advanced. True enough, there was a "dark age" following this youthful Western enlightenment; but it was imposed on Europe and resulted from the rediscovery, in the middle of the eleventh century, of Roman law.[2] As a legal system, Roman law was much more refined and more sophisticated than were the indigenous folk laws of Europe; and because the prestige of ancient Rome was still undiminished in the minds of men, it was not surprising that the rediscovered Roman law was uncritically accepted as the same law which had led Rome to its glory. In reality it was a rather degenerate version of it. It was Orientalized Roman law, as codified by the East Roman Emperor Justinian, at Constantinople; and the gist of it was contained in the sentence "The will of the prince has the force of law."

In other words, it was the law of Oriental despotism.

This in time became the chief instrument in the hands of the Roman Church (in many regards heir direct of Roman administrative tradition) in her attempts to make herself the supreme secular power in the Western world. If she did not succeed, she at least forced the secular powers in self-defense to counter the figment of the all-powerful papal rule by the grace of God with the fiction of princely rule by the grace of God. In the deadly, centuries-long struggle between church and state, the early political enlightenment of Europe became blighted and her ancient freedoms were suppressed. The search for the laws of God and of the universe gave way to arbitrary absolutism.

For all practical purposes the world of Western man was now rent in twain. On one side of the abyss dwelled nature, the epitome of everything untrustworthy, sinful; on the other dwelled man, no

longer a part of nature, but rescued from nature, or at least in the
process of being rescued. Man became a creature who, by special
divine dispensation, was allowed to stand all by himself, subject
to nothing but the will of God, that is, the caprices of a host of
self-appointed surrogates—divine, secular and ecclesiastical.

This pernicious late-medieval notion of man as living in a
cosmic isolation ward proved almost ineradicable. Perhaps its
most succinct and most corrupt expression is found in the seven-
teenth-century philosophy of Descartes, who virtually conceded
life only to man, while he saw all other creatures as lifeless automata. Even as late as the eighteenth century, so proud of its
enlightenment, we find the notion epitomized in Alexander Pope's
oft-quoted line "the proper study of mankind is man." If man,
this implies, just steadfastly contemplates his mirror picture, the
mystery of his existence is bound to be solved. And as regards the
social world of man, medievalism has held sway down to our
generation. It lives on, not only in every "modern" form of
spiritual and political dictatorship, but in the minds of most political manipulators, and even in some quarters of the "human-
ities." Nor need we be surprised at this, for until a generation ago
it was hardly permissible to regard human affairs as an aspect of
general science. Where this feat was attempted, as for instance
by the Social Darwinists, the results were worse than deplorable.
Social and political man therefore continued to claim autonomy
within a universe otherwise well-ordered by natural law.

Sooner or later, however, the fundamental question must be
faced: whether the concepts and the methods of science have any
bearing on the political world, or whether, within a civilization
predominantly molded by science, the sociopolitical sanctuaries
shall remain forbidden to science, a reservation in which the wild-
life of political instincts may continue to enjoy the ways of a
hallowed living fossil.

It will be conceded that the question is inseparable from that of
human freedom, that is, evolutionary freedom. For if the universe,
according to modern science, is of a piece and indivisible, so much

so that every elementary particle, without losing its identity, (theoretically at least) fills the entire cosmos, then science itself must be a unitary edifice of thought, and no domain of knowledge may be torn from it without introducing factual distortions. And since man lives in the same universe, he and his sociopolitical systems no doubt are somehow affected by universal law, and accessible to scientific interpretation. It is in this light that I propose to investigate the nature of man, i.e., as part of the universe of modern physics and as the most recent entrant on the stage of life.

Now, life is never static, else it would cease to be life. It is a one-way process, in which such parts as all of us may witness are merely animated moments of that larger process which began two billion years ago and to which biologists apply the convenient term "evolution." In any such process no momentary state is self-explanatory, but each is determined at least in part by the state that preceded it, and in its turn helps determine the one that follows. Nowhere, therefore, are the words of Francis Bacon (a paraphrase of Plato, incidentally) more pertinent than here, that "no one successfully investigates the nature of a thing in the thing itself."

Even freedom, though present from the beginning of the universe, has its evolutionary history. Indeed, decades before Darwin published the first acceptable theory of organic evolution, Hegel (1770–1831) presented in his *Philosophy of History* the very remarkable thesis that evolution, especially as it concerns man, is essentially the evolution of freedom. So we shall find it. If the foundation of the world were purely mechanical, there might never have been any life and little evolution.

These assumptions will determine our procedure. Since freedom, according to modern science, is not the exclusive prerogative of life, but is probably inherent already in the substratum of matter, it will be necessary to devote Part One of this study to a survey of the ways and means (as far as they are known) by which primordial freedom gave rise to life, to the further question of

the nature and extent of freedom in the animal world, and finally
to the question why only one member of the animal kingdom,
Homo sapiens, has attained a really appreciable measure of freedom. As will be seen, there are certain principles apparent at the
very beginning of life, even in molecular pre-life, which furnish
valuable insights into the life of man.

Part Two will elaborate some of the results gained in Part One.
On the one hand, it applies them to the question of the basic
animal instincts. On the other hand, it considers the roles of the
instincts and their relative importance in sociogenesis, particularly under those radically changed conditions when social relations
are no longer determined by laws of automatic physiology, but by
mental processes at least partly conscious.

The final section will attempt to integrate all previous results
in an evolutionary study of political civilization and to show to
what extent the laws and fundamental principles of nature affect
even the most highly evolved forms of life. It will be submitted
that on the understanding of the precise nature of these principles,
on our submission to the laws of nature apparent in them, depends the level of evolution our own civilization may attain, as
well as its temporal span of life. There is, according to this view,
and contrary to Spengler and Toynbee, no sound reason why a
civilization should not gain the "life eternal," provided it does not
flout the laws of life.

Since this evolutionary study ranges from basic physics to human
civilization, the middle ground, biology, must as a matter of course
occupy a prominent place and provide a good deal of our orientation. For much that is of crucial importance in the social world
has its roots in the biological stratum, just as the latter is rooted
in the physical. Obviously, though, biology cannot answer numerous questions relating to civilized human society. As life in general,
though still part of the physical world, evinces aspects which elude
understanding on traditional physicochemical grounds, so also
man, in rising above the common animal kingdom, came to face
problems which defy solution on purely biological grounds. Call-

ing them "social problems" is largely begging the question. A more fitting term would be "ethical problems." The most crucial problems of human relations are ethical by nature, hence we shall have to face the task of assigning ethics a place in the natural order. We shall recognize it as that still poorly understood regulator of living systems which begins to supersede physiological controls in evolution the moment these reach the point of diminishing returns. But its roots, we shall find, reach much deeper than the biological stratum of life. And it is probably the most important aspect of the problem of human freedom.

All prehuman levels represent stages in the evolution of something which, the new physics assures us, was there from the beginning of all things and a prime factor in the origin and spread of life. That something is freedom. For good reasons, many of our most eminent scientists have in recent years tried to make us aware of the fact that the universe can be understood only as a whole.[3] After almost a thousand years of aberration, resulting from the Orientalized Roman law and the ensuing absolutism, we have now returned to the indigenous point of view of Western man. And if the search for a basis on which to unify all sciences is still in its beginning, enough is known to permit perspectives which could be extremely rewarding in their application to human affairs.

It is the generally accepted view of modern science that life arose from an inert substratum, and it is as generally conceded that man evolved from purely animal, nonhuman ancestors. Both these assumptions presuppose what in the current terminology is called the complementarity of constancy and change, or of continuities and discontinuities. Unqualified constancy would preclude all evolution, and, conversely, absolute discontinuity in the events of the world would necessarily render futile all our attempt to understand them.

How much of this has any bearing on the evolution of civilized man?

Since it took place in the same world to which belong atoms and molecules, and since man himself in his physical aspect represents a configuration of atoms and molecules, these latter evidently constitute an important continuity in his evolution (in the sense that the same physical patterns are repeated continuously). Logic thus would seem to point to the conclusion that *in some way* the basic principles ruling in the lowest physical domain remain part also of the continuity of all evolution. Gravity might here be mentioned to illustrate the point. Though it seems to have no very great evolutionary significance, it is nevertheless responsible for the circumstance that even the headiest of humans must keep their feet on the ground and for the further circumstance that civilizations did not arise in the stratosphere.

There are fundamental laws of nature less obvious than gravity yet perhaps even more sweeping. The most basic and universal so far known is Heisenberg's Indeterminacy Principle, that remarkable achievement which in 1927 led to a decisive break with the fundamentals of Newtonian, or classical, physics. We shall deal with it at greater length in the following chapter. Here it must suffice to say that it refers to the relations of speed (or momentum) and location of an atomic particle. In classical physics, position and speed were always considered independent realities which could at all times be exactly determined. Heisenberg showed that in microphysics this is no longer the case. Position (p) and momentum (q) become aspects of a single event, related in such a manner that the more precisely p can be obtained the vaguer becomes q and vice versa. Hence the name Uncertainty Relation or Uncertainty Principle. While at first the respective formula was conceded universal validity, it is now held to be merely the expression of a limiting case of a still more universal one which, however, no one has as yet succeeded in formulating. The limitations of the Heisenberg formula lie in that it refers to an event involving only two factors (p and q). Such instances are of course rare or nonexistent in a universe in which, theoretically at least, everything interacts with everything. The case thus offers an exact parallel to Newton's celestial formula, which likewise applies only to two bodies, whereas he failed to formulate the total interaction of all the members of our solar system. And more than a thousand attempts since made to solve the famous *n*-body problem have been fruitless. However, the inability to formulate mathematically a fact in no way invalidates the fact. Even as a limiting case Heisenberg's equation, like Newton's formula, has revolutionized physics.

We now come to what will constitute the central theme of our investigation. It was Niels Bohr who first perceived the tremendous consequences of the fundamental facts disclosed by Heisenberg and he subsumed the inseparability or conjugate condition of location and speed under the term "complementarity."[4] This too will be dealt with in detail in the next chapter. Here I want only to point out that Bohr's interpretation of position and momentum as "complementary aspects" of a single unitary event (not as separable realities) has provided us with a philosophic insight of perhaps even greater significance than the mathematical formula from which it derives. The universality of complementarity is certain and easy to perceive even where the facts are too complicated for mathematical treatment. That is to say, it too applies to countless phenomena involving more than two interdependent factors. We shall therefore in the following distinguish between "simple" or "dimorphic" complementarity (cases with two constituent elements) and "multiple," "manifold" or "polymorphic" cases (involving *n* elements). Complementarity in general thus becomes a shorthand expression for the fundamental cosmic fact of the interdependence of everything with everything within any system, from the microscopic to the macroscopic scale. And all evolution can be viewed as simply the evolution of systems based on complementary interdependence. This is true to a limited extent of the evolution of purely physical systems and unconditionally true for all biological and social systems. Indeed, to the extent that this formulation holds, even political civilization becomes subject to universal law and reveals itself as something from the beginning potentially innate in the world's constitution.

Niels Bohr himself was the first to recognize the bearing of his principle on the problems of life, and as far as "simple" complementarity is concerned, I am in the fortunate position merely to elaborate his surmises. Nor are predecessors lacking who were aware of "multiple" complementarity. The psychologists have long referred to it as the Gestalt problem. Nor have the biologists been blind to the fact of total interdependence within organisms, though they have used a variety of designations for it. And finally, such national mottos as *"e pluribus unum"* and "One for all, all for one" prove that even clairvoyant men concerned with affairs social and political have long seen things in the same light. From microphysics to civilized nations the fundamental situation remains the same. The basic universal principle, then, which made evolution possible, is beyond dispute, though opinions may still differ as to the conclusions to be drawn from it. At all events, the time seems ripe for the abandonment of the late-medieval fallacy that the social and political spheres are beyond the pale of nature and can therefore be ordered in any arbitrary way.

As was mentioned already, this is not the first time that such intimate connections have been surmised between what is most evolved and what is most fundamental. The early Greek philosopher Heraclitus of Ephesus came very close to the concept of complementarity in his thesis of the *Harmony of Opposites*, in which he saw the world's dominant theme. The early Chinese philosophers knew it as the (static-female) *Yin* and the (dynamic-masculine) *Yang*, together embodying the basic truth of their universe. The Mazdaism of Zoroaster, and its adaptation by the Jewish and the incipient Christian world, coarsened it to a mere dualism, in which good and evil, God and the Devil, personified two hostile absolutes. But the notion reappeared in a form nearer the original one in the *coincidentia oppositorum* of the late-medieval cleric Nicholaus Cusanus (1401–1464). In early nineteenth-century philosophy (Fichte, Hegel, *et al.*) the principle was again served up in a degenerate form. Here Thesis and Antithesis were each merely the negation of the other, so that it took a measure of philosophical overbearing, of which only German

Idealists (and later the Marxists) were capable, to raise the Synthesis $(+ x - x)$ to more than zero. And finally, two jurists[5] of the first half of our century, both evidently unaware of Heisenberg, Bohr and microphysics, made the principle the basis of a legal philosophy. We are, therefore, in no way treading on virgin ground, but merely harvesting a fruit which, after almost three thousand years of growth, at last reached maturity.

PART ONE

Animal Man

*Such a task is intimidating—until it
is solved. Then the complexity is seen
to arise from multiple variations on
one theme, and to be less than
had appeared.*
LANCELOT LAW WHYTE

*It will be seen that many things we
tend to consider human can be derived
from physical theory.*
C. F. VON WEIZSÄCKER

1

THE COSMIC MATRIX

SAINT John might well have opened his gospel with the words "In the beginning was Freedom, and Freedom was with God, and God was Freedom." He probably would have come nearer the intent of the message of Christ and certainly nearer a scientific truth than by making "the Word" the beginning of everything. For, as we shall presently see, with the Heisenberg Indeterminacy Relation freedom became a scientifically acceptable concept, whereas it had been the great taboo of classical mechanics. More important, though, is this: the moment the notion of freedom became not only endowed with scientific respectability but a fundamental scientific concept, it became possible to think of integrating political science—to which, since the days of the ancient Greeks, freedom always meant so much—into general science.

THE OLD AND THE NEW PHYSICS

In order to understand the weathercock-like about-face of science, we must at least gain a general idea of the questions involved. We can be brief on this point, since many of the foremost representatives of the new physics have treated the subject in popular books.[1] But because there are still many who have doubts regarding the legitimacy of any connection between physical principles and the

15

highest spheres of life, it is worth stressing the fact here that even the old, or classical, physics was born of philosophy. Nor has there ever been a political system which was not the child of philosophy.

Classical physics goes back to two Greeks, Leucippus and Democritus (fifth and fourth centuries B.C.), probably the first men to search for a scientific basis which would explain all the happenings of this world. They came upon the idea of the atom and developed the first atomistic theory of the universe. They imagined the atoms to be the smallest individual particles of matter, of which all things, inert or alive, were built up. In addition to being indivisible, atoms were assumed to be unchangeable, hard little lumps of ultimate reality; not sovereign, but constantly buffeted and pulled about, united and separated by blind forces. The play of the forces of chance with the atoms was seen to be the prime cause of all happenings in the world.

In its essential features the theory has persisted into our century. But it really took the generation of its originators, and the generations following, by storm; for it was the succinct expression in physicophilosophic terms of the incipient first surge of individualism in the world (*individuum* is merely the Latin translation of the Greek *atomos*).

Now, if the atoms of matter represented ultimate reality, then that unit of the body social beyond which division could not go, single man, was bound to be of prime significance also. The theory therefore acted like a leaven on the compact heaviness of primitive ethnic groups and turned Greek culture predominantly into a glorification of the individual. To Roman jurisprudence it contributed its central concept, that of the person, without which Roman law could never have become the admiration of centuries to follow. Atomism even invaded religious thought, and in early Christianity blossomed forth in the dogma of individual salvation —whereas, according to the old Jewish view, God would either exalt or destroy the people in its entirety, in complete disregard of individual merits or demerits.

Thus, a theory of physics shaped an entire age in its social, political, artistic and religious aspects.

Nor is this the end of the story. Galilean–Newtonian physics was but an early mathematical elaboration of atomism. And finally, at the end of the seventeenth century, the theory served John Locke[2] as the matrix of a new political philosophy of uncompromising individualism, which became the backbone of British Whig policy and later of American politics. Somehow, the arbitrary separation of the world of man from that of nature was never completely successful.

John Locke's conviction, that the fundamental principles of the physical universe must have a bearing on the world of social man, grew out of a sound intuition, although, as we now know, he reasoned from defective premises. Of these, the basic physics of the twentieth century has allowed little to survive, so that an "updating" of our political notions in agreement with the new physics becomes a pressing need.

The old physics culminated finally in an absolute determinism, which received its most poignant expression in Laplace's hypothetical World Spirit who, theoretically at least, would be able to calculate every event throughout the universe if for one given moment all the atoms and all the factors working on them were known. The universe was a huge clock running down, nothing else. There was no freedom. Everything was predetermined.

This scientific philosophy received its unexpected *coup de grâce* in 1927 when Heisenberg published his Indeterminacy Relation. This brought about an almost complete reversal of what had formerly been fundamental in physics. In place of the old notion of mechanistic determinacy Heisenberg introduced on incontestable experimental evidence a simple-looking (only *looking!*) formula which, paradoxically, expressed the empirical certainty that in the final analysis there can never be any certainty, strict law, or sure prediction of events.

This indeterminacy is not just epistemological, i.e., it does not merely set limits to human knowledge, which it might be possible to overcome if more refined methods of investigation were devised. Indeterminacy is inherent in, and one with, the nature of subatomic phenomena. Here Bohr's complementarity (the circumstance that basically there is no such thing as an isolable "simple fact" but always a complex of at least two elements conditioning each other) appears to be the fundamental reality. As one physicist put it, indeterminacy is "the direct outcome of the principle of complementarity."[3] And this in turn means of course that a certain freedom is one of the elemental constituents of the physical world.

That a degree of freedom should obtain on the basic physical level seemed at first so by implication only, but further investigation soon left no doubt about it. An atomic particle displays an "independence" which would have been unimaginable within the lore of deterministic mechanics. The old, still popular image of an electron moving around the nucleus in a specified orbit proved erroneous. There is never more than a certain *probability* that at a certain moment it will be found at a definite location, a probability which is complemented by probabilities of its being almost anywhere within certain limits. The particle's movements are spontaneous, one might well say erratic, exhibiting a certain "innate freedom." For good reasons Eddington used the drastic expression that classical physics "foists a deterministic scheme on us by a trick."[4] Only where huge numbers of atoms are gathered in inert masses do the microphysical indeterminacies cancel each other and make rigid predictions possible, as in astronomy. Classical physics thus becomes a limiting case of the new physics or, in the words of Jeans, "Heisenberg's quantum mechanics is universally true, and the classical mechanics merely a special case of it."[5]

The term "quantum mechanics" for the new physics needs explaining. "Quantum" refers to Planck's "quantum h," the smallest energy "package" of the world. Fractions of it are unknown, for it always appears as unity or in multiples of unity. "Mechanics" in the sense of the new physics may seem self-contradictory. The fact is, though, that within an undisturbed atom there still reigns a well-defined order based on probabilities. In a statistical sense, a quantum-physical system, considered as a closed system, remains subject to dependable law. This is the reason why, despite all basic indeterminacy, there is stability in the world. If it were otherwise, there could never be either specific elements or stable chemical compounds. But individual microphysical particles defy all strict law, particularly as regards their spatiotemporal manifestations. Nobody can forecast what path a particle will take, and in the case of radioactive elements it is impossible to say which of many apparently identical nuclear constituents will next shoot off, or when, or in which direction. Moreover, microphysical determinism breaks down with any attempt to take measurements or under other interference.

The significance of all this for life should be obvious.[6] To repeat: the lack of determinism is freedom *of a sort*, even if, on the most basic level, it would be rash to project into it something resembling our own human feeling or consciousness of freedom. But it should not be too difficult to realize that even that primordial and essentially negative freedom represents a potential out of which in the course of evolution the freedom which man experiences could develop. Man, then, has not removed himself from what has come to be recognized as the cosmic matrix of all existence. He still remains a fairly rigidly determined physical system accessible (within limits) to physical interpretation. If he were not, he could not last long as an individual and his descendants would never resemble him.

The discovery of these facts occurred at a very propitious moment. Whitehead had just published his theory of organic mechanism, which defined "a primary organism" as "some particular pattern . . . grasped in the unity of the real event." Psychology at about the same time formulated related phenomena in the Gestalt theory, whose close affinity with the principle of complementarity is particularly noteworthy. "Gestalt" is "multiple complementarity." Thus, the new physics not only put all the physical sciences on a solid foundation, it also drew into its orbit biology and psychology by showing that they arise from the same matrix.

COMPLEMENTARITY

From the beginning the abolition of strict physical determinacy offered hope for a better understanding of the phenomena of life than had been possible from the viewpoint of classical mechanics. But perhaps the greatest service to students of life in all its phases was rendered by Niels Bohr, when he shifted the emphasis of the Heisenberg Relation from its negative uncertainty to the positiveness of complementarity. *Complementarity is indeed the most basic of all facts* and indeterminacy only one of its outer manifestations.[7]

Today it is, indeed, permissible to regard even the Theory of Relativity as a partial anticipation of, or pointer to, the theory of complementarity which dominates modern physics. Even relativity is an expression of uncertainty. The intrinsic relatedness of the two is undeniable. Einsteinian relativity arose from a reconsideration of the fundamental concepts of space and time, Heisenberg's indeterminacy from a reconsideration of the fundamental relationships of location and momentum (i.e., also of space and time factors). Of great significance, further, is the fact that since Minkowski's interpretation of Einstein's space and time as "space-time," the latter has become a unitary phenomenon with two complementary aspects, one static, the other dynamic. And finally, the two most surprising results of relativity, pre-Einsteinian and Einsteinian, conform to complementarity. These are the Lorentz–Fitzgerald contraction, i.e., the shortening of the length of moving bodies (in the axis of motion) and the time dilatation of Einstein, i.e., the slowing down of the "clocks" of moving bodies. Spatial contraction and time dilatation are "reciprocal" (in an exact mathematical sense) and reciprocity is a form of complementarity.

The main trend of theoretical physics today is to reduce everything to geometrical concepts, i.e., spatiotemporal relations. We nearly always coupled to the proton and the electron, which thus represent the elemental complementarity of matter. And always the normally positive proton represents a relatively huge and *immobile* mass, whereas the normally negative electron has a very minute mass (the proportion of the two masses is 1837:1) and is eminently dynamic. The two complementary forms of electricity thus embody the basic forms of *statics* and *dynamics* and reveal their relationship to space and time. But since electricity seems to be at the bottom of all things physical, including the phenomena of life, may we not expect these latter to reflect the situation presented by the proton and the electron? That is, may we not assume all living phenomena to be divided into relatively static and relatively dynamic ones?

What, for instance, might be the bearing of all this on the familiar fact of the two sexes which, it will be conceded, is not without importance in social and political life?

Physiologists have long held the answer in store for us and demonstrated that sex is an evolutionary variation on the fundamental theme of complementarity. If we follow them to where we can observe male and female denuded, so to speak, of all later complications, the connection between sex and electricity becomes quite clear. The simplest form of a male, the sperm cell, always bears a negative electric charge and is an eminently dynamic and self-propelling animalcule. Conversely, the simplest form of a female, the egg cell, or ovum, always bears a positive electric charge and is as immobile as a plant.

Even as regards mass, the same relation obtains between ovum and spermatozoon as between proton and electron. The positive-static ovum is always thousands of times heavier than the negative-dynamic spermatozoon. No more perfect agreement could be hoped for. So that it looks as if the proton was the prototype of everything immobile, positive, female, and the electron the microphysical "ancestor" of everything dynamic, negative, male. At the most basic level of life, then, egg cell and spermatozoon are the embodiments, respectively, of the static-positive "protonic" and

therefore cannot but begin to see in (relatively) static s
(relatively) dynamic time the most fundamental of al
mentarities and in complementarity itself the primal
the universe. All else results from it. All evolution, p
well as vital, thus becomes essentially the developme
elemental theme of complementarity. We shall theref
following chapters favor this aspect of the foundation
physics and investigate it as one of the principal continu

After these essential preliminaries we can now proce
familiar ground. The remainder of this chapter will be
showing, at least in outline, that the evolution of li
forms actually *is* the progressive complication of prin
mentarity, a series of ever more involved variations on

The ponderous term "complementarity" need not d
We have long been familiar with it in its simplest
one name or another. Polarity, for instance, known
from magnetism and from electricity, is an eleme
complementarity. In fact, it appears that electric pol
the most fundamental complementarity of the pa
one of the most basic continuities, and it is theref
qualified to start us on our quest. Its diverse mani
no longer be spoken of as mere analogies. Where
variations of a fundamental phenomenon, analc
priate. The apple which reputedly inspired Ne
mechanics did not drop on the physicist's head a
analogy of a meteorite falling from heaven. Apples
have a tendency to fall to earth because they ar
same universal law of gravitation. Neither is ther
saying that $20 \times 40 = 800$ on the analogy of $2 \times$
larity exists because of the periodicity of the deci
wise, there is, as we shall see, a certain p
evolutionary development of the fundamental f
mentarity. Basic facts and periodic variations to
sible for evolutionary similarities.

In the atom of modern physics, the two form

of the dynamic-negative "electronic" principle. Together they form the elemental complementarity of life, and both are equally important—aspects of a single phenomenon, which is the species. Without undue exertion we have suddenly come from basic physics to one of the basic facts of life, biological as well as social.

Nor has the range of the principle reached its limits in the sexes. The division of all life above the most primitive organisms into a vegetable kingdom and an animal kingdom reveals the same pattern. Plants are relatively static, immobile, protonic, their total mass on earth, figured in tons, is astronomical. Animals, on the other hand, are dynamic, electronic, embodiments of the loco-motor principle, and as compared with plants their total mass on our planet seems to be almost negligible.

We encounter what is principally the same division into a relatively static-protonic and a relatively dynamic-electronic mode in every living cell and every organism. In the cell the nucleus is the (relatively) more static part, the surrounding cytoplasm the more dynamic. Every animal has a vegetative system and an animalic system proper. These facts are mentioned here merely to complete the outline. They will be discussed in greater detail in the following chapter.

Finally, if we leave the purely organic stratum and rise into the superorganic or social sphere, we again meet the same basic organizational divisions, two sides of life complementing one another: the relatively static social sphere proper with its conventions and domesticity, largely dominated by the "vegetative-protonic" sex, the women, and the relatively dynamic-electronic side with its trade, science and technology, the life military and political, essentially preempted by the more animalic sex, the men.

Here again I will content myself with the mention of bare facts and reserve a detailed discussion for later chapters. But it is perhaps not superfluous once more to emphasize that this "repetitiousness" in evolution is not mere analogy. Nature does not work by analogy. It evolves by way of inventing variations on basic data, and complementarity is the most fundamental cosmic fact. Hence the primal bipartite structure of space-time persists throughout evolution, for all phenomena are articulations of space and time. The complementarity of space-time thus becomes the evolutionary principle par excellence. Analogy is never more than a mental crutch. To say that the principle developed here is based on analogy would be as inane as impugning the child for forming itself on the analogy of his parents. We are all of us the *progeny* of Mother Space and Father Time, not their imitators.

We therefore have every reason to believe that evolution represents a continuity of interlocking variations, ever more complex variations, on the fundamental theme of space-time, from particle and wave, through the plant and animal kingdoms up to human civilization. Every higher form contains the lower ones, so that from the atom up, every level is a maze of complementarities within and between complementarities or, as we have already termed it, a form of manifold, polymorphic complementarity.

We must now consider a further aspect of the primal principle. According to Heisenberg, neither momentum nor location of an elementary particle has any "reality" or "actuality" by itself alone, and both attain meaning only as conjugate aspects of the total event. If the physicist could obtain the absolute value of a particle's speed, his knowledge of its position would be zero—and the figure he obtained for the speed itself therefore questionable, since speed can be meaningful only relative to a position. Conversely, absolute position is incompatible with the concept of speed; hence, a particle without speed becomes plain nonsense and its location itself a hoax.

Nor is this aspect of complementarity confined to the lowest physical level. It appears to be of the essence of all complementarity, and this fact no doubt enabled Bohr to recognize its importance for the phenomena of life. We would, Bohr pointed out, kill an animal if we tried to push investigation to the point where we could study its atoms. "The least concession which in this regard we have to make to organisms is just big enough to enable them to hide, as it were, their secret from us."[8]

We find this side of the primal principle reflected throughout the evolutionary scale. Statics or dynamics, or space and time, in absolute form (if you can imagine such a state) would be the end of the universe, for either is but an aspect of something greater and more fundamental. Even dead matter evinces something akin to life, as is evident in electrical or chemical events. No plant is devoid of a certain motility, i.e., an animal aspect, and no animal is without its vegetative system. There is a man hidden in every woman and a woman in every man. That male and female are complementary aspects of the species is obvious from the fact that the extinction of one sex would also mean the extinction of the other. In brief, both members of a complementary pair are vital to one another, though one may be dominant, the other subordinate. In a much more intricate way all life is similarly interdependent in all its aspects and forms a unitary whole, manifesting manifold complementarity. Wherever we look, we observe the upshots of the same basic continuity of principle, not mere analogy.

PHYSICS AND SOCIAL EXISTENCE

We now come to contemplate still more far-reaching implications of physics' most universal principle.

Complementarity may be loosely characterized as a singular sort of relationship between at least two conjugate and inseparable factors, of such a nature as always to imply a measure of that unpredictability which is most familiar to us from the phenomena of life. In other words, the term complementarity has reference to a unique kind of *organization*. In fact, one would not be far wrong in calling it the prototype of organization. For if we try to delve below the strata in which complementarity is first apparent, we are facing a complete void, or chaos, conditions which offer the mind nothing to clutch at, no help in its efforts to orient itself. In brief, as far as one can see today, complementarity appears to be *the* primal datum, and already it is not a simple, but an *organized* fact, the constituent parts of which have no meaning by themselves alone, but only conjointly within the primal "organism." The term is here used on purpose. For, as already indicated, complementarity reveals its significance especially in its most multiple phases, in all those phenomena commonly called organisms.

Now if we look more closely into the unique nature of complementarity, we must recognize that there is innate in it a basic definition also of *integral "social" existence.* (A term less anthropomorphic than "social" would be preferable, but we lack it.) Metaphorically speaking, complementarity in its simplest form is the "marriage" of two diverse elements, their integration into a new superior entity. These conditions hold for all forms which in the very broadest sense of the term can be called "social," i.e., wherever there is integration of any number of different elements into an entity of a higher order, a new Gestalt. In all such cases we are dealing with simple or multiple complementarity and nothing less. Nothing whatsoever seems to be able to make its appearance in this world except on the basis of this one cardinal and universal principle. In the beginning was complementarity.

On this principle is based the nature of the microphysical particle with its dual wave and material aspect, the integration of various kinds of particles into atoms, of atoms into molecules, of molecules into organisms and of individual organisms into social systems. As a matter of principle the major difference between atoms and human societies is only one of organizational complexity. The process of complication leading from atoms to civilization is known as evolution. This, as we shall see more clearly in the following chapter, makes complementarity *the evolutionary principle par excellence.*

All evolutionarily vital organization rests on this basis. Hence the new physics' most fundamental principle becomes also the prototype of the "division of labor," or functional differentiation. Proton and electron furnish one of the elemental instances. Each is a specialist whose potentialities cannot be realized without its partner in the creative "marriage" of opposites from which the world has sprung. One positive proton and one negative electron, between them "dividing" a "field of labor," create the simplest atom, that of hydrogen. All the heavier, more complex, atoms, and above them the molecules, are merely elaborations of this basic case, more intricate variations on the fundamental theme. There seems to be no other way in which nature could become manifest.

I have the deep conviction that the reason why the greatest works of music impress us as revelations from beyond is that they make this process come alive in our presence. Musical genius seems always to have understood that all that is enduring in the world is theme and variation, modulation, thematic development, periodicity, continuity within change, the complementarity of point and counterpoint, of static chords lending poise and substance to the dynamic flux of melody. No other art allows us so intimately to participate in the creative process of complementarity. None other so vividly carries into our hearts the universe's open secrets.

The best proof that throughout the basic physical realm we are dealing with systems of multiple complementarity lies in the fact that the larger atoms are not merely expanded hydrogen atoms, but systems each evincing entirely specific characters, even though they are all built up merely of protons, neutrons and electrons. The increase or decrease of the number of particles beyond a certain minimum changes the atom completely. And in the molecules the substitution of one single atom for another can radically alter the nature of the molecule. Each of these systems is more than the mere sum of its parts.

It is hardly necessary today to postulate, in the manner of the biological school of the Vitalists, an autonomous life principle (*élan vital*, vital force, entelechy, etc.) in order to "explain" life. It puts much less strain on our credulity if we envisage the earliest forms of life merely as the ultimate manifestations of the principle of integrative complementarity, already at work in every atom, every molecule. The Vitalists were naïve enough to accept matter as something ordinary and self-explanatory, wherefore they had to make life the great mystery. Today we see the tables turned. With a sufficient acquaintance with matter and the aid of the primary formative principle of the world it is not too difficult to conceive a mental picture of the origin and nature of life. By contrast, matter has become a greater scientific secret than even man himself. The real mystery lies hidden in what subtends the palpable material world.

And complementarity, of course, is part of this mystery which will probably never be explained. Here we are at the very limits of human knowledge. At the same time, complementarity is the one side of modern physics that all of us can understand and which corresponds to familiar realities of our daily lives. We all know it in its simplest form in electric polarity, in the difference between plants and animals and between women and men. Beyond that, it is the essence of all creative evolutionary events, of everything that results from cooperation between "harmonious opposites." Above all, its great evolutionary significance lies, as we shall see, in the origin and spread of life, biological as well as social. The give-and-take of social life, the social division of labor, the inter-dependencies involved in all events of the economic sphere—between employer and employee, seller and buyer, producer and consumer, etc.—all are variations on the same theme. Wherever there is human productivity, creativeness, it rests on the same basis. It is the secret of all art, all science and invention. And finally, all religions (if we discount the external paraphernalia in which most have entrapped themselves) are essentially founded on the same deep consciousness of complementarity, of the fact that we are all part of each other, of nature and of God.

2

THE QUICK AND THE DEAD

I N comparing the approaches to life possible from the points of view of the new and the old physics, one is reminded of Occam's Razor. One good cutting edge goes a long way, while several edges to one blade are worth less than nothing. All attempts to interpret life in terms of the many fundamentals of pure mechanics got precisely nowhere, indeed always taxed our faith in the wisdom of science to the breaking point. By contrast, the one fundamental principle of the new physics takes us from nonlife to life in the easiest way imaginable. For complementarity itself is, so to speak, a living, organic principle. Furthermore, being of universal validity it cannot be subject to the Law of Limitations (which determines the maximal size of everything from an atom to a star) but can serve as an "escalator principle" transcending every threshold. And finally, as the archetype of integral organization it becomes the quintessence and sine que non of all evolution.

Complementarity is the great continuity between the foundation of the physical world and life. That there are discontinuities as well explains the differences we encounter everywhere. Life is synonymous with organisms, from whose singular nature is derived the concept of organization. Since the primary principle of organization is complementarity, whatever rests on it merits being called organic, everything deviating from it inorganic. In this

29

view, even atoms, founded as they are on the integrative complementarity of particles, become organic systems. On the next evolutionary level, however, that of the molecules, we encounter the
significant division between a class continuing the organic trend,
those molecules without which life is unimaginable, and the "side
line" of the inorganic molecules, representing the first evolutionary
cul-de-sac. The difference is so important it merits careful consideration.

INERT AND LIVING STRUCTURE

Even the investigation of the structural, i.e., the static, side of
organization in inert substances and certain material phenomena
on the borderline between the world of the dead and that of the
living can furnish insight into the nature of evolution and open
up to us valuable perspectives bearing on the nature of social
and political organization. In the evolutionary step from nonlife
to life we become aware of the first major "escalator" effect of
universal complementarity, its power to overcome all physical
limitations.

It is apparent that, by and large, the distinction between inert
and living systems is identical with that between relatively static
and relatively dynamic ones. And since this essay is also a natural
history of freedom and a dynamic system is "freer" than a static
one; since, furthermore, a trace of freedom seems inherent in the
basic constitution of the world, it is worth investigating how, on
the one hand, freedom could be increased and, on the other hand,
virtually be lost. Obviously, we would not be too far from the
truth in saying that in inert systems aboriginal freedom has been
sacrificed, whereas living systems have preserved it and developed
its potentialities. How does this become manifest on the static
side of basic complementarity?

The study of the architecture of the most common substances
has shown that virtually all solids are built on a very simple
scheme. Their patterns are symmetrical or "periodic," arrived at,

as Schrödinger[1] says, by the "dull way of repeating the same structure in three dimensions again and again." This group embraces the ordinary crystals, which make up the bulk of all substances. All possess the faculty of adding more and more atoms or molecules of the same type to their structures. That is, they can *grow*. Growth, then, is a property already of most inanimate substances and in no way the exclusive prerogative of life.

There is another class of crystal, however, in which the deadly monotony of pattern of the first group is avoided. These crystals show a structure which is quite irregular, asymmetric or "aperiodic," and they assign, so to speak, an individual role to every atom or group of atoms. This type of organization does not permit the indefinite repetition of a basic pattern, in the manner of a checkerboard or wallpaper design. Its dimensions are extremely limited, confined in fact to the molecular or submicroscopic scale. And here we come upon one of the most astonishing facts of the molecular world, a mystery for which physics has so far found no explanation. Since these crystals have rigidly imposed limits of size (they are in fact double crystals twining around each other like miniature vines, connected with each other at regular intervals by cross-links similar to the rungs of a ladder), they have developed the "knack" of overcoming these dimensional limitations by dividing lengthwise into exactly equal halves. Then, after this stunning performance, each half completes itself again into a full double helix. In other words, these molecules *replicate*, they engage in vegetative or asexual *reproduction* and multiply like living organisms, though they are still inanimate things. Again, something which was long believed to be a monopoly of life was anticipated by a class of inert microscopic crystals. They are therefore usually referred to as "living crystals." All viruses belong to this group.

At this moment in the grand course of evolution, then, we stand at the crucial point of the parting of two ways. This is Eddington's "great bifurcation"[2] between, on the one hand, the original course of asymmetrical or organic organization and, on the other hand, the simplistic symmetrical, inorganic or mechanical organization. Differently stated: the mechanical organization of common, symmetrical crystals means an abandonment of complementarity, while the asymmetric organization of organic ("living") crystals means the continuance and elaboration of the primary principle, the adherence, as it were, to "cosmic fundamentalism." From its very origin in space and time creative complementarity has always been based on asymmetry. In the strictest sense, therefore, it was not the "living crystals" (and life in general) which constituted a new departure. The deviant phenomena are the "inorganic" things. Life conforms to the fundamental order. Common inert matter, on the other hand, represents evolution's Great Dead End. The biological mechanists always looked at it the other way. Not only did they, evolutionarily, put the cart before the horse; they even tried, as it were, to evolve the horse from the cart.

Contrary to assumptions hitherto dominant, the "roots" of life, therefore, seem to go deeper than those of inert phenomena; the principles on which it is based are more fundamental than those of inert organization. This hardly means (as even Bohr thought) that specific "vital" elements are involved. Microphysical factors alone, some possibly still unknown but not supernatural, would probably be sufficient for our understanding of life. At any rate, even now they can fairly satisfactorily account for the evolutionary continuity between the microscopic and the macroscopic living world, whereas pure mechanism cannot. A generation ago the Russian biochemist A. I. Oparin, in his well-known study *The Origin of Life*,[3] stressed this continuity. The "origin" of life, he said, must not be thought of as the sudden and miraculous appearance of something absolutely new but should be recognized as part of the slow evolution accompanying the gradual cooling off of our planet during perhaps two billion years.

But to come back once more to the vital difference between the asymmetry of organic molecules and the symmetry of the inorganic ones, we can briefly sum it up thus: in the organic-asymmetrical ones complementarity has been preserved, whereas the inorganic-symmetrical ones have sacrificed it. It seems appropriate here to give a few indications of the unique functional importance of the differences between the two categories. They far transcend the molecular level. Symmetry is generally static, whereas all dynamics, all happening, all evolution depends on asymmetry, i.e., on material inequalities and energy potentials. This is true even of those manifestations of life to which men have traditionally attributed the highest values. Marriage and love are absolutely unthinkable between complete equals. We cannot imagine a work of art, be it a poem, a novel, a drama, symphony or great painting embodying absolute symmetry. A single fully symmetric sentence could convey no meaning but would be a senseless juxtaposition of words. We understand now why these and similar human phenomena were always held to be the supreme symbolic utterances of life. By contrast, the mathematico-physical formulae relating to dead matter are all symmetrical, they are *equations* and have proved completely useless in scientific attempts to probe to the bottom of life. Furthermore, to point out another aspect of this problem, in the "dead" crystals symmetry is also coupled to egalitarianism, the mechanical side-by-side of identical units. One can remove any unit without effect on the whole structure other than to make it slightly smaller. Not so with the "living" crystals. Here the nature of the whole depends so much on the exact position of each of a variety of different units that none can be removed, or change position with another, without altering the character of the whole. In other words, the parts complement each other, they form an integral Gestalt representing more than the sum of the individual units. The first significant step, then, from death to life, apparent in these crystals' faculty of reproduction, is identical with the extension of (multiple) complementarity from the atomic to the macromolecular level. Rigid egalitarianism, depending as it does on symmetries, is inimical to life and evolution—for the reason, of course, that egalitarianism by definition precludes complementarity and thus allows no trace of that precious correlate of complementarity which we call freedom. We shall find this truth corroborated even in the sphere of civilization.

THE ORIGIN OF LIFE

To the biochemist, life is what goes on under the skin of the organism. This seems much too narrow a point of view. From the very beginning, organisms would have been impossible without the environment or, more precisely, that part of the world which after the origin of life became the environment. The reason is that the environment gave birth to life through a process of self-differentiation. The two have remained part of each other ever since, inseparable, mutually dependent, "imprinting" or "conditioning" each other. In short, they were always a complementary pair. Although the problem of how an inert world could produce life is still far from solved, we are not quite in the dark. In agreement with general scientific theory we may assume (to repeat) that no otherworldly magic was involved and that life arose spontaneously when, after millions of years of gradual climatic changes, the proper conditions were present on earth.

What, then, were the preparatory events? When the original ball of glowing gases had cooled off sufficiently, it stratified into a still-hot core of the earth, constantly torn by volcanic eruptions, the virtually boiling ocean and a steamy gaseous atmosphere. It was the "hot thin soup" of the seas which became the mother of life, for it contained in itself, or derived from volcanic exhausts, all the elements necessary to the simplest organic compounds: carbon dioxide, hydrogen, oxygen and ammonia. From these, more complex organic substances could form, and in nature probably were formed under the influence of volcanic heat and lightning. Among these higher organic compounds are the amino acids, the building blocks of still more complicated molecular structures, such as proteins, nucleic acids and others. Many of these have been experimentally produced in the laboratory, up to molecular weights running into the thousands.[4]

But what is especially interesting is that, if dissolved in water, assortments of these organic substances show a tendency to coagulate and to form microscopic, or even larger than microscopic, globules, in more than one way looking and behaving like bacteria. They are not, however, true living beings. Presumably, such pseudo-organisms existed in the primordial ocean and were the first distinct *individuals* in an otherwise diffuse medium. One even has reasons to believe that some chemical reactions took place in them which heightened still more the resemblance to life. These were, though, most probably, disintegrative or fermentation processes, condemning these forms of pre-life to a very brief existence. We can perhaps best formulate their impermanence by saying that they embodied synthesis and analysis in successive phases. These little gelatinous blobs arose out of the environment and again dissolved in the environment without leaving a trace behind. They had no descendants.

It is clear that, however complex the chemistry of such pseudo-organisms might have become, without a radical departure in a new direction there would never have been life on earth. What was needed was something more fundamental than chemistry: a lasting mutuality between the sea and its creatures. Not the consecutive giving and taking back, but a simultaneous give-and-take, the integration of synthesis and analysis. In other words, a complementary relationship between creatures and environment. Chemistry alone can never describe life. The *organism-environment complementarity* defines the very essence of it, the end which chemistry serves. When this "leap" into a new existential dimension took place is of course impossible to say.

What was also needed before true organisms could appear were certain macromolecules capable of acting as organizers of the millions of other molecules that make up even primitive cells, giant molecules more stable than the others (as the management of firms had better be more stable than the crews working under them). How all this came about nobody knows. The details are fantastically bewildering. But the principles are not quite beyond

our reach, and we can at least bring the event closer to our understanding by means of an anthropomorphic fable.

It looks, we might say, as if some of the large organic molecules
in those ephemeral pseudo-organisms had said to themselves, "If
we as a group cannot help constantly paying out to the environment, why shouldn't the environment give us something in return?" This is putting it crudely and is, we repeat, but a piece of
fiction. Still, it brings out the crucial point. And we may add,
continuing the fable, that the "idea" of these "clever" molecules
proved successful. They became the executive molecules of the
first true organisms. They managed to stabilize the cell system,
direct its internal affairs and thus indirectly stabilize the material
exchange between it and the environment in an intricate and
well-regulated give-and-take.

Though we want to avoid becoming too technical, we must at
least show that our little fable has a realistic basis and that *life
does represent an extension and elaboration of the principle of
complementarity*.

The typical living cell, the basic unit of life, consists of two
main divisions: the central nucleus and the surrounding cytoplasm.
They are united by a very intricate harmony of physical and chemical processes and in every regard represent complementary opposites. The nucleus within its membrane, its "stark conservatism"
and its electric positivism could almost be called a serene monas-
tic island within "the rough-and-tumble world" of the surrounding cytoplasm with its negative electric charge. These systematically opposite characteristics reveal them to be evolutionary
variations on the themes of space and time, statics and dynamics,
of proton and electron, the atomic nucleus and the electronic
mantle. The nucleus, as the relatively conservative-static part, embodies in its genes the characteristics of the species which are
carried over unaltered from generation to generation, even through
millions of years. The cytoplasm, on the other hand, mediating as
it does the material exchange with the environment and the adjustment to the changing environment, is, as we shall see later,

much more versatile, indeed it can become a revolutionary factor.

Complementarity determines virtually every functional and structural detail within the cell. Above we spoke of the "executive molecules." To these belong the DNAs (deoxyribonucleic acids) and, to a lesser degree, the RNAs (ribonucleic acids), which in recent years received so much publicity because they embody the "coded messages" directing reproduction and metabolism. They too represent complementary pairs interacting by way of feedbacks, with the RNAs functioning exclusively in the cytoplasm, the DNAs mainly in the nucleus. Furthermore, these immense molecules each consist of a double helix (like a circular staircase), the two strands of which also stand in a complementary relationship.

These are all examples of dimorphic complementarity. But since the cell embodies millions of molecules, all integrated into a fabric of mutual interactions, even the simplest organism obviously represents one of the most fabulous forms of manifold dynamic complementarity. The molecular biology of it, especially of the cytoplasm, if we could observe it with our coarse senses, would probably remind us of a thousand beehives commingled to perform thousands of different but interlocking complementary functions.

The living cell, then, on the one hand merely extends the world's basic principle to new limits of complexity. On the other hand, however, this extension does involve a "leap" into something new: the application of the same principle to the relations of a physical system and its environment. Internal complementarity of *closed* physical systems existed since the origin of the first atom. Complementarity of *open* physical systems and the environment was the greatest revolutionary event on earth. *It is identical with life.* The physicochemical processes of the mascroscopic sphere for the most part are sporadic, soon ebbing out into a "stability of form." By contrast, the dynamic complementarity of organism and environment, tied into the internal complementarities by countless feedbacks, is what determines life as a "stability of process or of functions." This is the decisive fact. Even so, as a novel set of complementarities, life merely continues an ancient evolutionary trend, as the following summary table shows.

Universe: Complementarity of space and time.[5]

Particle: Complementarity of matter and waves.

Atom: Complementarity of nucleus and electronic mantle.
Complementarity of particles.

Molecule: Complementarity of diverse atoms.

Cell: Complementarity of microphysics and macrophysics.
Complementarity of nucleus and cytoplasm.

Life: Complementarity of organism and environment.

The very essence of life is complementarity of organism and environment. It cannot be understood on any other basis. This may not tell us much regarding the internal organization of the cell, on which all biochemical investigation has been concentrated. Yet internal organization becomes completely meaningless if we overlook the environment. Again, the internal organization of the cell alone can throw no light on the evolution of higher, multicellular, forms of life and the social organizations of multicellular organisms, including those of man. These higher forms of life are intelligible only as still further extensions and elaborations of the principle of complementarity,[6] as will soon become apparent.

If now we return once more to our little piece of fiction, we may conclude it by saying that the revolutionary "plot" of those "clever" giant molecules bore the result that the constant losses *to* the environment of groups of molecules became compensated by an equally constant selective taking up of atoms and molecules *from* the environment, units of a higher energy content than those given up. Molecular combinations which once had formed merely to disintegrate again now could be maintained as "steady states" or "equilibriums of flux." They became self-maintaining, self-regulating, self-healing and even self-perpetuating living creatures.

To some it may appear too incredibly naïve to reduce the origin of life to such a simple formula as the complementarity of a physical system and its environment. Such an attitude is itself the result of the naïve assumption that life must be "explained," and the insinuation that the above presentation pretends to be an "explanation" of life. Nothing could be more erroneous! For the simple reason, of course, that primal complementarity has never been explained either. We can but humbly accept it as the metaphysical *prima causa*, or something very close to it.

ORGANISM AND ENVIRONMENT

Life, then, is organism-environment interdependence. Where this relationship disintegrates, death ensues, whether the prime cause be a spontaneous internal disorder or a changing environment to which the organism cannot adapt.

By far the most significant result of the novel organism-environment complementarity lies, not in the purely physical, but in a supraphysical plane. It brought with it certain "emergents," those usually impalpable, immaterial and hence purely qualitative concomitants generally associated with the rise from one evolutionary stage to the next higher. In our particular case the emergents associated with the origin of life are the qualities we call *psychic*. For the first time, then, in earth's history there appeared atomic-molecular configurations with a kind of awareness of something outside themselves—the environment. In other words, with this novel organism-environment relationship there also arose the still mysterious and much abused body-mind complementarity. In some way, but inevitably, the fact of the dynamic external liaisons of the cell evoked as its correlate *within* the cell a sort of preconsciousness, however tenuous, something which is logically quite impossible in a strictly closed system. Where the environment is not an integral part of a physical system it cannot have any kind of correlate or "representation" within the system. A stone, being completely self-contained, needs no mind. But where the environment is an integral part of the physical system, there is bound to arise within the system something that stands for the environment, as its correlate or representative, an overseer of the interactions. This is not mere speculation. It is intrinsic in the phenomenon of complementarity. We can derive it from complementarity with the same surety with which Leverrier forecast the discovery of a new planet (called Neptune after the discovery) on the basis of Newton's theory of gravitation.

The birth of consciousness, then, coincides with the origin of life. Life is consciousness, as consciousness means life. Body and mind are but two aspects of the same phenomenon. Even in its most dilute forms (as in the case of plants, for instance) consciousness is essentially awareness of the interaction between organism and environment. One might say it is complementarity becoming aware of itself. This was the event which began to convert part of the purely physical world into a world of life and of ever greater awareness of life.

Here again, as in the case of life itself, it should be stressed that if this interpretation throws some light on the nature of mind, why living things have it, whereas dead things lack it, we have not really explained it. That it is a flower of the evolutionary process, of this there can be no doubt. It emerges at a certain stage of earth's history but, emerging, it may in some other form have existed before. As a concomitant of life, of a highly complex form of the primal principle, mind still, in Sherrington's words, "goes therefore in our spacious world more ghostly than a ghost." We would have to explain the Wherefore and Why of the origin of complementarity to explain mind.

After the origin of life and consciousness, the further evolution of life presents itself essentially as the unceasing elaboration of the organism-environment complementarity. Of all the features that distinguish living from nonliving phenomena this complementarity is the most important. It epitomizes everything that gives meaning to life. No living system can therefore be self-contained, nor life ever be bottled up in an organism. It can only be understood as an integral organism-environment relationship. Shut off an organism from its environment and you have killed it, because you have deprived it of its vital complement, what Emerson[7] called "this shadow of the soul, *or other me.*"

Now, since, as we saw, freedom was from the beginning an upshot of complementarity, the increasing complexity of involvements in the organism-environment relationships of evolution also could evince increasingly greater freedom in the ascending scale of life's complexities.

It might be alleged that, by making itself dependent on the environment, the organism did not gain but sacrificed freedom. A comparison, say, of a grain of sand by the wayside and a mouse skipping over it will bring home the fallacy of the argument. The grain of sand does not depend on the environment, yet it is not it which is free enough to skip over the mouse.

At bottom, it comes down to this, that in the organism-environment interdependence the environment from the outset is vastly more than meets the eye, for it is, theoretically at least, never smaller than the universe. And since the relationship in question was from the beginning that of complementarity, it always entailed at least the organism's chance to enlarge its immediate environment by elaborating its interdependence with it and thereby to realize more and more of the potentialities inherent in the larger *Lebensraum*—that is, the universe—to become attuned to ever new, and more, aspects of the world holding out chances of greater freedom. The complexity of the open organic system thus becomes a measure of the degree to which the integration of organism and environment has progressed, a symbol of how large a share of the potentialities contained in the universe has been realized by the organism.

Stated in still a different way: every organism becomes a record in living flesh of the extent of its vital *concerns*. It mirrors on a minute scale that part of the cosmos on which its well-being depends, which has acquired "meaning" for it. And the organism's concerns become an indication both of its dependence on, and its freedom from, the environment.

Life's great potentialities always lay in the environment which, according to basic science, is never smaller than the universe. Every organism therefore is oriented to it; for, briefly, the environment means fulfillment. The relations of organism and environ-

ment therefore are much better characterized as a "draw" than as
a "drive," as E. W. Sinnott[8] rightly saw. And much that has so
far been taboo in conventional biology and psychology thus becomes a legitimate integral of the philosophy of organism: di-
rectiveness in organic events, goals, purposes[9] (though we may
never identify these with their human equivalents) and, on the
highest levels, hopes, dreams and aspirations. This may be metaphysics, but the basic physics of today has become almost inseparable from it. Freedom itself is a metaphysical concept. As Henry
Margenau said, "The metaphysical wealth reposing largely un-
tapped in modern physical theory is enormous and challenging to
the investigator."[10] The once fairly clear demarcation between
physics and metaphysics has vanished.

To illustrate this I will refer to at least one phenomenon.
Descartes had partitioned the world into the subjective ego, the
objective world and God, the latter so far out of the picture as to
be of no concern. This remained bed-rock science for three hundred years. Now the new physics is breaking through the once-
impenetrable Cartesian bulkheads everywhere. The separation of
subject and object has become untenable. And, whereas until recently it was, to say the least, most indecorous on the part of a
scientist to have recourse to the concept of God, the latter is
today met with quite frequently in the discourses of the more
philosophical of the great physicists. Here too complementarity
has opened new frontiers. We have seen that it is intrinsic in the
organism-environment complementarity that the environment
have within the organism a representative something whose manifestations we experience as consciousness. But it is likewise intrinsic in this situation that the organism have a representative
something in the environment. And if we take environment in its
fullest and truest meaning, in the sense of the cosmic whole,
without which we could not be, we unavoidably arrive at that
concept which men have at all times designated by the name of
God, or the world soul, Brahma, extrahuman spirituality, or even
Jeans' God the Mathematician. God, the world and its creatures

have become part of each other. It turns out that some of the medieval mystics were closer to modern thought than Descartes, for they held it to be one of the central truths that God needs man as man as much as man needs God.[11]

MAN'S ENVIRONMENT

Though we shall later find ourselves facing the question of the environment again, now, while its vast significance is fresh in our minds, is the opportune moment to broach its meaning for man. This opens up a rather breathtaking perspective, the scope of which offers the best testimony to the magnitude of the environmental factor in evolution.

All evolution is essentially the elaboration of the one primal and universal principle. The primary element of life is the single cell. Its relation to the environment is based on the simplest, dimorphic, form of complementarity. Now, the higher, multi-cellular, organisms have one-sidedly elaborated this basic situation. The many cells among themselves are held together by bonds of multiple complementarity, whereas their relationship (as an integrated unit) to the environment is still in the nature of simple complementarity. But as soon as the environmental side of the situation becomes as complex as the multicellular individual itself, we reach the level of life usually called *social existence*. Human civilization represents the highest, most involved form of multiple complementarity among multicellular individuals evolution has brought forth. We shall never grasp the essence of social evolution and social existence with all they entail unless we realize that they represent a continuation of the working of the most fundamental of all formative principles.

The organism's concerns, we said, are an indication of its dependence on the environment, but also of its freedom from the environment. This is nowhere as obvious as in the case of man. He has chosen to concentrate his concerns on the most incredibly intricate part of his surroundings—his own kind. Himself from the beginning one of the most involved of all creatures, he has come to depend on the cooperation, direct or indirect, of, and with, a large section of his own species; which, reflecting back on him, made him a still more intricately organized being, the most universal of all.

But far beyond merely making the species the dominant aspect of his environment, man has tremendously elaborated the organism-environment integration in that he extended it over the species, or at least a considerable part of it. In a much more significant measure than any other creature he is comprehensible only within the species, at least the cultural community to which he belongs. R. M. Yerkes said of our nearest animal relation that one chimpanzee is no chimpanzee at all. This truth is even more pertinent with regard to man. An absolutely isolated human is inhuman. As the astonishing freedom of even the most primitive cell (in comparison with dead matter) can be understood only on the ground of organism-environment complementarity, just so man has achieved his even more amazing freedom by putting himself into the most complex of complementary relationships with his fellowmen. Man's singular form of organism-environment relationship thus turns out of be, above all, *species integration.* Herein lies part of his "secret," and also the reason for his freedom.

Social and political organization, then, must be regarded as merely the most involved elaboration of a condition which is identical with life: the give-and-take between a living being and its outer world. No matter how sociologists and political scientists may look at the problem, from the point of view of a unified evolutionary theory (and evolution *is* a single event) there seems to be no other possibility but to look at sociopolitical organization essentially as species integration, which, as we shall see more clearly later, of all forms of integration holds the greatest potentiality of freedom, because it permits the most intense development of the fundamental condition of freedom—complementarity.

A single cell is already an apotheosis of complementary complexities and beyond comprehension. In the face of individual man, with his thousands of billions of cells more intricately organized than those of any other creature, all superlatives fall flat. And hundreds, thousands, millions of humans interlocked into a single system of mutual dependence and cooperation are even more beyond the power of descriptive words. Here, probably, the universe has reached the apex of elaboration of the basic cosmic theme, and hence the greatest measure of its concomitant—freedom.

We begin to see that the philosophic foundations of the new physics have implications for all levels of life, up to the world of civilized man. The freedom which in the basic stratum of the physical world is mere indeterminacy, absence of strict law, in the course of evolution became creative freedom, the freedom to organize living systems in ever more intricate ways; the freedom to widen the concerns and the interests of living beings, to let them develop in a measure ever larger the potentialities inherent in the world. This, then, is the road along which was evolved a creature free enough to draw upon all the resources of this planet and to begin to unravel the secrets of the universe and of himself.

At the bottom of the world's order there is ruling a sort of particularism, which is progressively sacrificed in the evolution of the common inert structures formed of periodic aggregates—the collectivistic material systems, as we might call them. But the primordial order regains importance with the rise of aperiodic, or organismic, crystals, in which an individual role is assigned to each atom or group of atoms. Life, finally, with its individualism, is in a way the full bending back to, the coming into its own again, of the particularity of basic physics with its indeterminacy, its spontaneity. Life is not collectivism based on the additive principle, but *integration* of true *individuals* into entities of a higher order. Equals can never be integrated, only added up.

Thus—and this is especially important in its political consequences—while there can never be complementary integration of identical and egalitarian units, true integration always respects the uniqueness of the individual and is in fact impossible without diversity of individuals. So that for two important reasons we may justifiably say that life, in all its unfathomable complexity, has stayed closer to first principles than have collectivistic inert aggregates; it has remained truer to the fundamental cosmic order; or, as theologians would probably put it, life has remained closer to God than dead matter. The physicist Pascual Jordan[12] stated the matter thus: the laws of life are the more universal as compared with those of inert matter, which represent merely special or limiting cases.

Since we stressed the fact that life can probably never be explained on purely mechanical grounds, it should be added now that even organic evolution makes use of mechanical devices. Internally the essence of the living cell, like that of the atom, lies in the complementarity of indeterminate microphysics and mechanics. In the human organism, too, innumerable processes can be explained as mechanisms: the intricacies of the hormone system; the homeostasis or equilibration of the bloodstream maintained by mechanical feedbacks and many nervous processes; bones are almost entirely mechanical affairs and some of their features correspond exactly to the stress-and-strain curves of construction engineers. But the crucial vital processes will probably always remain beyond an exclusively mechanical interpretation. As a matter of principle, *all mechanical processes are reversible. Life has never been found so.* And regarding the two basic sides of modern physics, relativity and quantum theory, the concept of reversibility, i.e., of mechanics, has lost all meaning. The foundations of the world are nonmechanical, one might even say organic or "organismic." Hence every strict mechanization means, or threatens to become, a deviation into a new evolutionary blind alley. The animal instincts (Chapter 4) will furnish impressive examples, and certain aspects of social evolution (Chapter 8) offer related phenomena.

3

FREEDOM IN THE ANIMAL WORLD

A s was pointed out in Chapter 1, the term "freedom" came back into the purview of science with the advent of the new physics. There are, though, still many scientists who deny it any *raison d'être*. Others find it useful, even necessary. It may belong to those common words on which, Heisenberg says, ultimately all understanding rests because they alone touch all human reality—whereas science never deals with more than selected aspects of it. However that may be, we shall use "freedom" in a twofold meaning, both justified by the new physics. In the first place, it stands for that indeterminacy physicists have discovered to be part of the substratum of the "material" world and which appears as the concomitant of complementarity. In the second place, we shall regard it as a potential, as something which, conjointly with the elaboration of the mechanical aspects of organisms, is itself amenable to development. We are aware, though, that, since complementarity by definition rules out absolutism, any kind or degree of freedom life may attain must always be tempered by its necessary complement—some mechanism or law.

All this—since life developed from inert matter subject to strict mechanical law—makes it necessary to gain some insight into the conditions and the unfolding of freedom in the animal kingdom if we would understand the meaning of freedom for the world of man.

FREEDOM AND ENVIRONMENT

The organism, we said, is an integral part of the environment and vice versa. Both are complementary aspects of a larger something. Hence, since freedom is a concomitant of complementarity, at least one aspect of animal freedom must be linked to the organism-environment interdependence.

This conjugate condition of organism and environment, the incessant give-and-take between them, also makes, of course, the environment dependent on the life it supports. The water in a glass bowl in which a goldfish has lived for only a fraction of a minute is not the same water it was before the fish was put into it. The fish has "conditioned" his new environment. On a much larger scale the same thing happened with the ocean after life began.

Terra firma went through a similar process of conditioning. During aeons of time, when the oceans already were swarming with myriad forms of life, the continents were still expanses of stark, naked rock. But once the most primitive forms of plants, the algae, had established a foothold on land and prepared it for the invasion of animals, the transformation of the continents into what we know them to be progressed apace. This transformative ability of the organism, arising from its complementary interdependence with the environment, is part of the freedom of life, and an aspect of what in the last chapter we called the potentialities of the environment.

But precisely because the environment is the prime datum, out of which the organism-environment complementarity evolved by a process of self-differentiation, it remains, of course, the more powerful determining factor. So powerful is it, indeed, that the sea, from which all life originally sprang, to this day conditions the life of everything existing on the continents. Even man is able to live on land only because he carries in his lymph and bloodstream a fragment of the salty ocean which gave birth to us all.

The transition from sea to land[1] offers perhaps the outstanding illustration of the truth that animal freedom, despite its dependence on the environment, is above all the freedom to explore, and to realize the potentialities inherent in, the environment. It is well, therefore, to make clear what is meant by the potentialities of the environment.

THE SEA AND THE LAND

The fact that millions of years ago a primitive ancestor of man abandoned the sea and made itself at home on land embraces an enormous part of the history of human freedom. As the mother of all life, the sea, by and large, is as unsuitable an abode for higher forms of life as is the waterbag known as the fetal sac for an adult human. To this day the sea has remained the home only of primitive forms of life. There are neither flowering seaweeds nor highly intelligent marine animals. No octopus or shark is intelligent enough to be trained for the circus. The most advanced of the ocean dwellers, the reptiles and aquatic mammals, are backsliders, whose constitution was molded on land, but who at a later time were lured back again into the baser salty milieu by its more ample food supplies.

The view was prevalent until recently that all aquatic creatures whose ancestors never left the water are deaf and dumb, but it had to be abandoned (fishes, e.g., possess a hearing sense and utter communicative sounds). Still, their sensory equipment is of a lowly order. A fish never knows what it sees, so you could never teach it to read. This brings us to the chief means of maintaining and elaborating the relations between organism and environment: the sensory apparatus, the animal's "intelligence service," the means, as it were, of exploring the potentialities of the environment. Above all, the senses inform the animal concerning the whereabouts of food, the presence of enemies, or of members of the other sex, virtually the only parts of the environment for which a primitive creature like a fish ever evinces concern. A wedding ring or a telescope would mean nothing to it; because, briefly, it does not have the brain to unravel the significance of such things. It could never have attained such a brain because, for one thing, it lacks eyes of sufficient refinement to make possible a brain able to interpret detailed visual reporting. And the fish is devoid of good eyes because they would be wasted on an aquatic creature. Water is a much more opaque medium than air, so that all water dwellers live as in a perpetual fog. Only in the clear atmosphere over land was the evolution of acute vision and hence of a good brain possible, because only here does acute vision "make sense."

This is but one instance illustrating to what tremendous extent the organism reflects the potentialities of the environment. The higher it stands in the scale of evolution, the larger is the part of the environment which it reflects, for which it evinces "concern." In other words, an organism's concerns offer a measure of the degree to which it has become integrated into the environment, but also a measure of its freedom. The animal with a well-developed sensory equipment is not so much at the mercy of the environment as is the less-developed creature; it is a freer being. Whereas plants and the lowest zoological phyla are almost completely at the mercy of their surroundings, man, ranking highest in the evolutionary scale, can modify it almost at his pleasure.

Here the question must be countenanced: how was it brought about? If life began with microscopic specks of integrated "living crystals" floating aimlessly in the sea, how could a creature like man be evolved from them? The answer is again complementarity —in the form of "cooperative division of labor," which, of course, need not be conscious.

COOPERATIVE FREEDOM

In the foregoing chapter we referred to that general rule known as the Law of Limitations, or law of thresholds, according to which no kind of structure or organization can grow, or be extended, beyond a certain maximum. The rule is valid from atoms to solar systems. One can build a little toy house of cardboard and let it drop to the ground without damaging it, but a cardboard house of "natural size" would collapse of its own weight. A forty-story brick house would require walls so thick as to leave little usable space inside, wherefore skyscrapers have to be reinforced with steel skeletons.

We encounter the same situation among organisms. If elephants should grow much larger, say twice present dimensions, they would become so clumsy and immobile as to be unable to gather the minimal ration of daily fodder. Similar intrinsic limitations hold down the living cell to microscopic size. Because the surface of a body increases as the square of its linear dimensions, whereas its mass increases as the cube, the surface of an expanding cell would soon be too small relative to its mass, and it could then neither absorb enough oxygen, nor eliminate all the metabolic wastes.

Beyond all doubt, the most crucial problem in the evolution of life, after the rise of unicellular organisms, was to find ways and means to achieve larger than microscopic dimensions, that is, multicellular organization.

Its solution could evidently be found only in a principle without narrow intrinsic limitations—and again complementarity proved to be the answer. A first step in this direction is to be seen in the tentative stage of loose-cell societies, swarms or schools. If part of the freedom of organisms is to be found in their power to condition the environment, to make it "a better place to live in," many cells living in close proximity could do the job better than a single one. One such organism, for instance, dropped into a poisoned medium is doomed to die, but many organisms in the same medium can secrete enough antidotes to neutralize the poison. A swarm can survive where an individual would perish. This has been demonstrated even with goldfish.

The next experimental step is represented by the slime molds, the organisms causing dry rot. Normally these go about their feeding grounds like other swarms of Protista. But then the incredible can happen: apparently upon a certain signal, thousands of these free-floating cells suddenly converge and grow together into a wormlike creature with a distinct front and rear end. Like an animal of a higher order, this "composite being" then "marches off" the scene with a purpose. Certain of the cells transform themselves into spore-bearing (reproductive) organs which, when the creature arrives at its destination, release the spores. In due time these again become amoebalike cells living as a loose swarm and the cycle of life begins anew. Here we have an illuminating example of how the quasi-accidental or passive cooperation of a mere swarm becomes active cooperation between member cells of the same species. The widening of the scope of life and of freedom which this entails is evident in the purposive "marching off" of the new animal.

But the really decisive advance in evolution began with permanent multicellular organization. It brought about something for which one is tempted to use expressions such as "change of attitude" or "change of outlook." Whereas the single cell is still a relatively isolated microscopic focus of material exchange in an environment which is largely inert, the many descendants of a single cell clinging together of necessity came, so to speak, to "focus their attention" upon each other. Certainly for the cells in the interior of the cluster the decisive environment now was no longer "dead nature," but living sister cells, which were bound to condition each other. This led to a controlled internal environment. And this interdependence and integration of many cells is of course nothing else than the extension of complementarity from the unicellular to the multicellular level. Cooperatively these cells could control a much larger environment than a single cell, or a loose swarm of cells, could. This was their gain in freedom.

There are other notable aspects of multicellular, or metazoan, organization. First, since many cells are now cut off from the outer, sustaining, environment, their functions can no longer be exactly the same as those of cells on the surface, or of single cells. A diversification of functions is therefore bound to take place; and this division of labor among many cells again is nothing but an aspect of our fundamental theme. More important still is another point. All these coherent cells of metazoans, being descendants of one mother cell or egg cell, belong of course to the same species, no matter how different they may look as a result of their having assumed different physiological functions. The multicellular organism hence represents the first stage in the great evolutionary trend of *species integration*, which achieved its highest level in what is customarily called the social animals. It means nothing less than the trend to extend the principle of complementarity over entire species.

It is quite pertinent, therefore, here to misquote Abraham Lincoln and call the beginning of multicellular organization the first attempt at government of the species, by the species, for the species. As Lincoln saw the greatest potential freedom in political organization of his definition, so also the freedom of life is dependent on the degree of species organization achieved by each kind. On all levels of life this means a diminishing of the influence of external factors, an increase in internal control, in self-regulation, self-government, which even in our political world we take to be largely synonymous with freedom.

FRUITS OF COÖPERATION

We must regard it as very fortunate that neither Darwin nor Alfred Russel Wallace was a slave of the microscope, or we might still be without a halfway satisfactory theory of evolution. The microscope, assuredly one of the most valuable tools of research, is not without its drawbacks. There was a time when biologists expected almost everything of it and thus allowed the tool to thwart their mental perspective. Because microscopic comparison showed many protozoa to be vastly more complex than any cell dissected out of a multicellular organism, the theory arose that multicellular evolution was possible only at the price of cell degeneration.

Modern biology has abandoned this view. Sherrington,[2] for example, one of the great physiologists of this century, among many eminent workers in the field, emphasizes that in all vital respects the member of a multicellular system is fully the equal of its distant solitary cousin. But we may safely go further and sum up the whole argument in the statement that, by and large, higher forms of life are possible only on the basis of higher-ranking constituent units. What the microscope did not reveal to those early investigators is that members of multicellular bodies have raised *cooperation* to a new high level. This is the reason why they are in a position to call their own a great deal that is far beyond the reach of the single cell. A digestive cell, for instance, manufactures enzymes for the benefit of the whole community *in addition to* those it secretes for its own needs. It still takes care of its own respiration, metabolism, elimination and reproduction. Hence it is much more than a tiny cog in a monstrous machine. Cooperative cell existence has in fact raised it to a higher category than that of the isolated cell and given it a "fuller life" by far.

The matter of size is not unimportant either. Generally speaking, smallness alone means inefficiency, because there is never enough surplus energy to amount to anything. A single cell has a relatively enormous surface and wastes a great deal of energy by heat dissipation. Try to imagine, for instance, what this means to an amoeba, which reproduces about every forty-eight hours and thus must work hard enough to double its weight in two days. In this regard, integrated cell communities represent an extraordinary gain, for the larger and better organized they are, the greater is the saving of energy, and therefore the chance of survival. This is clearly reflected also in the diminishing rate of reproduction in the ascending evolutionary scale. Birds and mammals flourish without having to reproduce every other day; they have gained free time, time not taken up by the bare tasks of survival.

Finally, consider what multicellular organization means with regard to the highest of all freedoms, those gained through the sensory-nervous system, especially vision. I single out vision because it has opened up to us the most astounding share of the potentialities of our environment. A solitary cell may be sensitive to light stimuli, but it positively cannot *see*. The simplest act of objective sight presupposes a complex eye and a brain center capable of receiving and interpreting the nervous impulses reaching it through the eye, all of which demands a minimum of millions of integrated cells.

The unique nature, then, of those radiations which we experience as light is one of the potentialities of the environment which the human organism has made the most of. The ordinary sounds and smells of nature are all events of this small planet and rarely travel farther than a few miles. No creature can hear and smell the moon and the stars, but we can see them. Light has made that part of our environment which we can consciously experience coextensive with the universe.

Visible rays can give us a far more "realistic," detailed and all-round description of near and remote objects than could diffuse sound and smell. As the neurologist W. R. Gerard[3] has beautifully shown in a famous paper, vision alone, being the only truly descriptive and the most universal sense, could in its highest sublimation become *mental vision*, insight and reason. The greatest part of all this "play of light" in us takes place in the form of images and visions, and *imagination* and *visionariness* are names we have given to the most advanced forms of thought. Thought— "don't you *see?*"—is essentially the ability to perceive and formulate relations revealed by vision. And since most of the relations shaping the objects and events which in evolution have conditioned our ways of thinking are of a complementary nature, even thought turns out to be essentially complementarity risen to consciousness.

The origin of words like *thought, think, know, knowledge, wit, wise, ken, keen, idea, speculation* and many others proclaims the truth that "to see the light," to "have an illumination," is synonymous with understanding; they are all derived from roots denoting visual perception. And on this abstract vision, the supreme revelation of the relational nature of life, depends the largest part of human freedom.

None of this is within the reach of a solitary cell. The foremost animal freedom and the loftiest "biological living standards" are the prerogatives only of rather large, complexly integrated multicellular beings, in which each of billions of cells serves all the others. In the words of a great biologist, William Patten,[4] "The growth of freedom ever awaits the growth of service. Freedom grows only so far as the instruments of service grow in power to serve and only so far as they actually perform their service. To the amoeba, the jellyfish, or the worm, the 'world' is the franchise of an hour in a drop of water, a niche in the rocks for a season, or a home in the sea for a decade. To man the 'world' is the universal whole of time and space, for their contents are his to explore."[5]

This, too, may sound to many like anthropomorphic analogizing. In truth, it is all the upshot of that one universal principle, complementarity, of which cooperation, integration, and division of labor are basic aspects. It is therefore no exaggeration to say that every cell within a higher organism is as free as any solitary cell and lives as full a life. More important, however, is the fact that the energies freed by cell integration bring forth those new phenomena characterizing higher levels of evolution and better integration with the environment, of which the supreme example is human thought.

As in the field of vision, free energies of cells within the acoustic system emerge as the faculty of hearing, which makes possible spoken language, the expression and exchange of thought, which again furnish the basis for the integration of multicellular humans into multipersonal systems, the ultimate stage of species integration and the most far-reaching elaboration of fundamental complementarity.

ADAPTABILITY

Adaptation is primarily the organism-environment complementarity regarded from the point of view of functional efficiency. One may distinguish two types of adaptation: the direct response (in Toynbee's terms) to the challenge of the environment—this is the most frequent and the more elementary kind and is exemplified by the evolution of fins in fish, of legs in land animals, and of wings in insects and birds; and what might be called the transcendent response, as it were, giving the environment more than it asked for—the evolution of thought from vision and of thermal regulation in birds and mammals would belong to this category.

Adaptation is one of the most important aspects of evolutionary theory and an almost inexhaustible subject. Here we only touch upon it to bring out the fact that the complementarity principle determines virtually everything. There is, hence, hardly an aspect of the anatomy, physiology, or the behavior of an animal that has any meaning without the environmental complement. Since all life originated in the sea, sweetwater organisms had to develop adaptive devices to prevent excessive salt loss. The "contractile vacuole" of some freshwater protozoans (probably familiar to most readers from elementary biology) is one of these. It is a tiny bubble which fills up with excessive water, carries it to the surface and "bails it out."

In general, all sweetwater bodies call for greater adaptability than does the ocean. Not only are they less salty but, being much smaller, subject to greater fluctuations of temperature and therefore of oxygen content. But precisely because sweetwater is a more exacting environment than the sea, it was destined to become the preparatory school for the university of life on land with its still greater demands and greater potentialities. Even man in all his aspects essentially mirrors this habitat. Nothing can come within his experience if it does not have in the human organism a tangible or intangible correlate, if man has no "organ" for it.

Always, therefore, adaptation means an extension and elaboration of the basic principle, the establishment of rapports with new environmental aspects, the development of new organs, new physiological processes, of finding new gene mutations to organize the innovations.

These remarks refer particularly to what above was called the "direct response" to the challenge of the environment. As an example of the "transcendent response" let us briefly consider the stabilization of body temperature and the relative freedom from the environment it has conferred on the highest Vertebrata.

In no habitat are there such fluctuations of temperature as in the gaseous atmosphere over land. The evolutionary problem they posed was one of the very last to be solved. Since body heat is a by-product of metabolic processes and of muscle activity, which are never constant, birds and mammals have instituted neuro-muscular, glandular and insulating devices to increase heat production during low phases of activity and exposure to cold, and heat escape mechanisms to use during very active phases and external heat.

But these regulatory inventions alone would never have sufficed to maintain constant temperature. A new type of blood with a more efficient oxygen carrier had to be originated. Oxygen being a gas, its solubility in water varies *inversely* as temperature, whereas the speed of physiological processes varies in *direct* ratio to temperature. Cold-blooded animals are therefore at a double disadvantage, somewhat like a man always wallowing in money when there is nothing to buy and with never a dollar to his credit when goods are plentiful. For in high external temperatures, favoring rapid metabolism, their blood can never supply enough oxygen, whereas at low temperatures the oxygen in the blood exceeds the requirements of the throttled cold-weather metabolism. The hemo-globin of the red blood of birds and mammals disposes of this problem, in that it permits a steady oxygen load forty times greater than would be possible without it and thus greatly facilitates thermal regulation.

In its turn, as the English physiologist Joseph Barcroft[6] pointed out, thermal equilibration alone could furnish the basis for the evolution of the conscious mind and mental self-control. It alone provides the internal constancy and calm which in the uppermost brain is necessary for the microelectric ripples of thought to weave their delicate patterns. It is almost entirely responsible for man's freedom to explore and employ the potentialities inherent in his environment.

The entire immense complex of such equilibrating factors (regulation of temperature, of blood sugar content, salt content, content of water, calcium, oxygen, fat, proteins, etc., etc.) is often referred to as Cannon's homeostasis.[7] And it can hardly be doubted that the physiological household presents us in this phenomenon the most incredibly involved biological variation on our basic theme.

So that, since Bohr's complementarity already implies interdependence, division of labor, cooperation, integration of two or more factors, "social" conditions (using "social" in the original meaning, denoting "things inseparable") evidently were no novelty at any stage of evolution. In this sense, all evolution is social evolution. Life could never have arisen on any other foundation. It is, therefore, a far cry from the "necessary evil," which Laotse, the Greek Cynics, Hobbes, Locke, Rousseau, Schopenhauer and others saw in every kind of society, to the real nature of "social" integration. If nature had tried to evolve according to the notions of these philosophers, it would never have brought forth anything living, least of all philosophers, who, like other creative minds, by their very existence bear testimony to the greater freedom which is the concomitant of increasingly complex forms of complementarity.

Even the one-sided and briefest of abstracts of evolutionary history so far given should suggest that the new scientific theory is not restricted to the purely physical realm but is of fundamental importance also for the origin and spread of life, biological and social. Without the unbroken continuity of at least one universal, an "escalator principle" like complementarity, not tied to any limitations, evolution would have been impossible—or would have come to a halt where a less than universal principle reached the point of diminishing returns.

4

INSTINCT AND ANIMAL FREEDOM

L EST the foregoing chapter leave the impression of having been penned by an enthusiast, it should now be pointed out that the evolutionary road to freedom never proceeds smoothly and in a straight line. It is tortuous, full of turnoffs leading into blind alleys. There are thresholds, at the near side of which dwells stagnation, while the far side monopolizes the future. The last and most formidable of these barriers is animal instinct.

The term "instinct" has often come under attack and many other designations have been substituted for it, all of which themselves mean no more than labels stuck on something the nature of which still largely eludes us. It seems preferable to stick to the one-fig-leaf technique of covering up our scientific shame, and the original fig leaf serves as well as any other. Provisionally, though, we may regard instinct as a special, or limiting, case of intelligence, immanent in every living creature.

HOW INSTINCT WORKS

We have seen that all higher animals develop specialized apparatus in charge of environmental relations: the sensory organs. Since their foremost task is to inform the animal regarding the whereabouts of food and reproductive partners and to warn it of danger, they are in the first place the tools of the instincts, and

60

these latter reveal themselves as the basic regulators of the organism-environment complementarity, the animal's most vital concerns become articulate.

Every animal is concerned with the preservation of this relationship, which means life, *self-preservation*, expressing itself in the
alimentary and the defensive instincts. The individual, however,
is short-lived; it can continue beyond its death only in its offspring
and therefore must reproduce in partnership with a member of
the opposite sex, which is also part of the environment. These
relations are governed by the sexual concerns, which are those of
species preservation.

In self-preservation and species preservation we again encounter
a complementary pair. If every individual would stop feeding and
defending itself, there would soon be no more reproduction, and
if reproduction stopped, there would soon be no more feeding
and self-defense. From our point of view the complementarity of
self-preservation and species preservation is one of the utmost importance, the consummate significance of which, however, we shall
only learn to understand once we consider its bearing on social
and political evolution.

Every instinctual concern, then, governs the animal's relations
with a specific aspect of the environment. Each evinces a behavior
pattern determined by mechanisms of the creature's anatomy and
physiology. By using expressions like "determined" and "mechanism" (which need not be taken too literally, since there are
usually certain modifiers) we have already indicated that there is
little freedom in instinctive animal behavior. And this is exactly
what makes *instinct the crux of the problem of freedom* and a
major roadblock in the way to higher evolution, especially, as we
shall see, in human society.

Anatomically man is an animal with all the main animal instincts. Yet he has gained an appreciable measure of freedom. He
may even make a cult of freedom and fill libraries with books on
the subject. That he can do it seems to attest to the fact of actual
human freedom, and certainly no other animal has achieved as

much. Evidently, the difference is identical with one of mental stature. No mind, no freedom. It would thus appear right at the outset that there exists an inverse ratio between instinct and thought. The more the one dominates, the more the other recedes; so that where instinct is nearly absolute, there is no room for thought, nor freedom.

The physiological interpretation of instinct given by von Uexküll,[1] as far as it goes, agrees well enough with our basic assumption to make it useful as a starting point. According to this biologist, an instinct pattern is like the working of an electric circuit. The animal itself is one pole, the environmental object which concerns the instinct the other. The two are complementary aspects of a single event. Anatomically, physiologically and behaviorally there must be reasonably close integration, the manifestations on both sides fitting like a lock and the proper key.

Let us assume the two poles of this circuit to be a cat and a mouse. For the cat, the mouse is essentially a combination of "field marks" (shape, sounds, movements, smell, etc.), which the brain center for sensory reception communicates to the brain's effector center, which then gives the signal for the start of a definite chain reaction. The mouse is caught and eaten. This is the pattern of the *food circuit*. Because the field marks trigger off the instinctual mechanism they are often referred to as "releasers." Now suppose the environmental object to be a boy throwing stones. The circuit takes on a different pattern: the cat flees. But if the object is a dog and the cat a very bold one, cat may attack dog. These two possibilities—flight and fight—are alternatives of the *defense circuit*. Finally, if the subject is a tomcat in February and the object a receptive female, the polarity between the two, constituting the *reproductive circuit*, may lead to a mating.

Now it is of peculiar interest that these events are all sporadic and of brief duration. Indeed, as von Uexküll points out, in every case the very purpose of instinctive action is to avoid further action.[2] We may liken these happenings to thunderstorms, in which an electric polarity arises between the earth and the clouds, soon to result in fulminant discharges, in *short circuits* annihilating polarity.

It must be obvious that, since the instincts are the prime governors of relations between organism and environment, and since all evolution depends on lasting complementary ties, the instincts in their raw form contain an inbuilt inhibitor of permanence. One of the foremost problems of evolution hence was to overcome this limitation, to devise ways and means to progress from repetitive short circuits to relational or functional continuity. This problem has so far received scant attention. Yet it may well be said that failure to solve it is part of the reason that made animals remain "mere animals," while man became truly human only to the extent that he solved it.

The animal, then, is so constituted as generally to reduce active relations with the environment to merely sporadic moments. Between these moments the average wild animal seems to have few or no concerns. It appears fully self-sufficient, living imprisoned within itself. Its environment is a vague area of space in which, if necessary, it can gratify its needs, but which otherwise is a dark, meaningless, closed world. This, however, is true only of the higher animals. The picture changes considerably if we descend to the lower realms. Earthworms, ants and mice, for instance, never seem to get enough to eat, and microbes, too, feed almost uninterruptedly. This incessant feeding is imposed on them by their diminutive size, the fantastic losses of energy implicit in the relatively enormous surface of a small mass. Large animals, on the other hand, represent a tremendous saving of energy. They have to eat relatively much less and can afford to retire within themselves for long stretches of time.

The essence of life being organism-environment complementarity, and evolution never anything but the elaboration of this fundamental relationship, the "retiring" of animals from the environment evidently constitutes one of life's dead ends, a termination of essential evolution and with it a curtailment of the potential freedom which is implicit in complementarity.

In order to see these facts in the proper perspective it is necessary to recall the difference between a protozoan and a metazoan. The latter, we saw, has substituted for part of the uncontrolled environment of the unicellular creature a regulated internal environment, and the external relations of the solitary cell have become extensively supplanted by an intricate pattern of internal relations between billions of variously specialized cells. That means that originally rather diffuse environmental relations have become *institutionalized* in concrete organs and organ systems.

If this sounds somewhat abstract, an example should make the meaning clear. In the last chapter we mentioned the contractile vacuole of freshwater protozoans which guards them against the dilution of the internal salt concentration. The contractile vacuole, then, is an internal organ (it has been called the most primitive form of the kidney) and yet in a sense it is no organ at all, for it lacks permanence. It lasts for only the duration of a single functional act, then must be replaced by another. In the case of the amoeba this is true even of the alimentary apparatus. At the approach of a morsel of food the little creature first has to improvise a mouth to take up the food particle. The mouth, when closed, transforms itself into a food vacuole which digests the food. This done, the digestive bubble drifts to the surface and remodels itself into an anus which discharges the indigestible part of the food. From beginning to end, an alimentary system— mouth, food vacuole, anus—is improvised for every morsel of food taken in.

This continuous improvisation of temporary organs is wasteful, and the higher animals economize by establishing permanent systems, the prerequisites for which are huge numbers of cells, division of labor, cell integration. The cases cited have their parallels in the domains of defense and reproduction, with which we shall deal in a later chapter. Suffice it here to point out that an essential part of evolution is the conversion of sporadic instinct circuits into internal physiological events localized in permanent organ systems; and that the intricate organs of higher animals—digestive, defensive and reproductive—represent nothing less than *institutionalized environmental concerns,* communal institutions of cells for the better regulation of vital functions.

What bearing has all this on the animal's freedom?

Evidently, such organismic "institutions," especially alimentary systems, make the animal independent of the environment for considerable periods of time. The tiger which has swallowed its prey need not worry for the rest of the day where the next meal will come from. Some snakes and fishes can in one single gulp rush through a banquet that will dispose of the food problem for weeks. These animals can retire within themselves and sleep, or just lie in their lairs, or in the sun, or float in the water and do nothing. They are temporarily "free," while the less well organized creatures must forage day and night.

But there is an obverse to the matter. Once the food reserves are used up, once hunger forces the animal again to turn its attention to the environment, the "freedom" which internal organs have bestowed upon it vanishes. The awakening of appetite, which becomes articulate mainly through reflex mechanisms, *ipso facto* excludes freedom.

The animal, therefore, is "free" only when withdrawn within itself, when its instincts are dormant, but when they are awake, when the animal is most alive, it is almost as unfree as a machine; its instincts keep it trapped in a vicious circle. Only one thing has proved a saving factor in this great animal dilemma: thought. And only man has to a modest extent been able to make use of it.

INSTINCT VERSUS MIND

Animal instinct manifests itself essentially through reflex actions which no amount of imagination can associate with the notion of freedom. Moreover, instinct is "blind," to the extent at least that it is "focused" exclusively on those environmental field marks which act as triggers on the reflex mechanisms. The more primitive the animal, the less it sees with open eyes if it is, so to speak, drawn into the vortex of a primal environmental event, when it becomes reattuned to a certain environmental aspect.

Consider the example of a spider. As Tinbergen[3] puts it, the spider never sees a fly objectively "as a fly." The latter can be two totally different things to the spider and evoke different reactions. Inside the web the fly is food, its struggling motions releasing the spider's preying instinct; outside the web it is an enemy evoking the defensive instinct and causing the spider to flee. The female spider shows the same seemingly conflicting types of behavior even toward the male. At the onset of a reproductive phase she recognizes the male as a male and accepts its service. But when her sexual want is satisfied, the male becomes just another insect and a "free meal."

Other animals present much the same picture. The male stickleback, a small fish of shallow waters, in its nuptial dress has a brilliant red throat and belly, which act as releasers on both the female and on other males. Again according to Tinbergen, any fish with a red belly becomes the male stickleback's rival; it is promptly attacked if encountered inside the male's own territory, whereas outside its own territory it puts the male to flight. Never, apparently, does a male stickleback see another male of the species as a whole; its instinctive visual center reacts only on the releaser. A dummy, the most clumsily fashioned decoy, so long as it has a red belly, will call forth the same reactions as a living rival. Thus, primitive instinctual behavior is never attuned to a situation as a whole, but only to a specific part of it. It is never really intelligent reaction, because largely based on a sort of push-button mechanism as unfree as anything.

Von Uexküll[4] has introduced the metaphor of the "environmental tunnel," which I prefer to call the "instinct tunnel." As soon as a releaser mark appears in the environment of an animal in which an elementary want clamors for gratification, the world at once narrows down to a tunnel between the animal and the releaser, enshrouding all the rest of the environment in darkness and effacing from the animal's consciousness everything but that one mark, or combination of marks, appealing to the instinct.

That this may have serious consequences should not be hard to see. Even if instinct be regarded as a specific, or limiting, case of intelligence, its dominance at a certain moment means the virtual suppression of what broader intelligence an animal may normally display. Its full intelligence therefore can become apparent only when the raw natural desires are kept at bay, when the environment is free of tension, slack. The following instances will illustrate this.

First, an example from my own observation. Cyril was an extraordinarily affectionate kitten of about six months. He would immediately run to his mistress if called, but he showed his greatest speed when he heard the clinking of his saucer. He had negotiated the stairs hundreds of times, alone and accompanied; yet when he was on the ground floor and heard his name or the clinking of his saucer upstairs, he completely forgot the stairs, though they were in plain view, and tried to reach his object on the shortest route—by jumping on the back of a chair and attempting to scale the wall.

This forgetting or overlooking, under instinctual tension, of something familiar and plainly visible is a typical deficiency symptom and well-known to us all. The awakened instinct momentarily debases the animal to a lower level of cerebration. Man, too, is wont to lose his head in such situations and is no longer "his own free self."

Another example, taken from Köhler's[5] work on the intelligence of apes, can give us further insight into these problems. The chimpanzee Sultan is locked into a cage containing two rods, neither of them long enough to reach a banana lying outside. After some abortive attempts with each rod, Sultan gives up, turns his back on the banana (his "sour grapes") and finally begins to play with the rods. In this playful mood he succeeds in sticking the thinner of the two rods into the heavier and, with a sudden about-face, eyes the banana again. The rods fall apart, but he quickly puts them together again and draws the banana into the cage. More bananas are brought and he secures these too. But the "angling" game itself now appeals so much to him that he neglects to eat the fruit and in the exuberance of his discovery pulls into the cage all sorts of objects, bundles of straw, rags and other things.

Two important points are to be noted here. First, the "idea" of making one rod out of two occurs to Sultan only after he has dismissed the banana from his mind. Second, after he has obtained and eaten some bananas, when appetite is satisfied, angling for all sorts of objects becomes of interest in itself; the "instinct tunnel" opens up, widens. Sultan's field of perception now comprises objects of no concern to his instincts. A new, richer world is open to him and rouses his curiosity as to what else the rods and those inedible objects might serve for. His intelligence is given *free play* and he begins to refine the technique of play. In a state of relaxation the animal becomes open-minded, world-aware in a sense never possible in the narrow tunnel of an instinctual event. In brief, Sultan becomes a freer creature.

It is evident from this case that freedom has two aspects. On the negative side it is the freedom from instinctual stress, and on its positive side the freedom to devote attention to noninstinctual aims, to the countless objects and traits of the environment that have no bearing on food, sex, or defense. In other words, the positive side of freedom is first of all freedom to *see* (also to hear, smell, feel, etc.), in general, to maintain the nervous system in a state in which it is most perceptive, in form, creative. And this, on the very highest level of life, means nothing less than the freedom to *think*.

Aside from being a matter of internal, anatomico-physiological organization, freedom therefore is largely conditioned by externalities, in so far as they obstruct or facilitate reflection, observation, thought. The most favorable conditions, as will become presently apparent, are provided by a social environment, because, in the light of our basic concepts, such an environment perforce makes the individual an "open system," not merely in a physiological, but especially in a psychological sense. In human society the freedom of life, from the beginning so intimately identified with open systems, has reached its broadest scope. In developing mind far beyond anything animals attained, man found a way out of, or past, the evolutionary dead end of instinctive mechanisms. The conscious mind represents the highest manifestation of the organism-environment complementarity. And its development became possible only through the extension and elaboration of species integration from the multicellular to the multi-individual or social level. Novel and revolutionary as this step may seem, it is, though, only the application of complementarity to new domains. But this unqualifiedly makes everything characteristically human and not merely animal in man, including his greater freedom, the concomitant of social organization.

Gustav Bally,[6] a Swiss psychiatrist, has set forth this side of the complex problem of human freedom in a study to which some of these chapters owe a good deal. He lays great stress on the fact, established by animal psychology, that subhuman creatures generally play only where and when circumstances free them from the merciless tyranny of instinct, and that among animals this situation is encountered only during the brief period of life when the mating call has not yet sounded and when food and defense problems are taken care of by parental solicitude.

With regard to food, e.g., Konrad Lorenz[7] has shown that normal animal behavior is essentially determined by reflex mechanisms. But in the protected parental environment, young animals develop a great many playful variations of the biologically inherited action patterns, variations unknown to adult animals and to the immature themselves if they are plagued by hunger. As a string stretched taut between two points can assume only one form, that of a straight line, whereas a slack, resting twine may fall into an infinity of varied curves, even so instinctive behavior in a "slack" field is capable of variation. And whereas interest in an instinctual aim ceases with its attainment, in a field at ease objects become endowed with sentimental and intellectual values, and interest in them is sustained until fatigue overcomes the animal.

Never, therefore, do animals appear so close to us in spirit as when they play. At such moments we are inclined to think them endowed with greater gifts than is their true share. This is the time, the only time, when animals live, as it were, experimentally, as free explorers of possibilities, trying out patterns of life beyond the hereditary rut.

Animal play, then, is in truth the symptom of a still mobile, unfrozen, evolutionary frontier, the visible disclosure of a plastic mental state during which, one feels, animal life could be guided to levels of existence unknown as yet to the species. Animal play is animal intelligence in action. As a rule, however, the fluid evolutionary frontier apparent in animal play congeals into rigid hereditary patterns upon the advent of reproductive maturity. Then the young are handed over to the ruthless totalitarianism of their instincts. Social life within the animal family gives way to a rather solitary mode, with the consequence that a living system that had been mentally open contracts into one open in the main only physically, and in its relations with the outside world almost bereft of freedom, because those relations now are governed by physiological mechanisms.

What all this means is that the largest share of potential freedom can be realized only if those conditions are preserved in which animals play: social conditions, an environment of mutual attention, the guarded security of interdependence. That human freedom in particular is completely determined by these conditions is a fact which will engage our attention to the end of this inquiry.

PART TWO

Social Man

*In producing life, cosmic evolution
overcame its own bounds; in giving
rise to man, biological evolution
transcended itself.*

THEODOSIUS DOBZHANSKY

*For a science of man, the problem
is not whether or not to have
anything to do with values, but
how to devise satisfactory methods
of studying them and discovering
how they work.*

JULIAN HUXLEY

5

HOW FREE WAS PRIMITIVE MAN?

Throughout Part One of this study it was our endeavor to show how complementarity subtends biological evolution and in its "escalator capacity" made it possible for the purely physical to "overcome its own bounds." Our next task will be to find some elucidation of how "biological evolution transcended itself." The answer has already been suggested: by continuing to build on the primal principle, which is organic, man kept to the main course of evolution and avoided the dead ends of mechanism. Once more to quote Dobzhansky,[1] "the superorganic stands in a relationship of interdependence with the organic. Human evolution is the singular product of interaction between biology and culture." Interaction always means complementarity.

We have therefore reached the point where we must inquire into the precise means and ways by which man, physically a zoological phenomenon much like any other, managed to separate himself from the rest of the animal kingdom by a gulf so vast as to justify his putting himself in a category all his own. Here it is well to bear in mind the vicious circle of the instincts in which animals are trapped. As adults they are free only when least alive, when freedom is of little use. But the moment instinct beckons an animal to enter the environment as an active agent, when freedom would seem to be most valuable, it vanishes almost completely.

There was a time, hundreds of thousands of years ago, when our own ancestors were little more than animals, the most intelligent primates probably, but still essentially nonhuman animals. In fact, even today the vast majority of men subsist on an almost shockingly animalic level, concerned with little else than the gratification of their instincts, with food, drink, security and sex.

THE MYTH OF FREE AND INDEPENDENT MAN

Yet so perverse have been prevailing notions that for the past three hundred years most of our social philosophies and many political systems have been founded on the assumption of an aboriginal "free and independent man," each one a king in his own right. It was a solemn article of dogma that the self-sufficient sovereign individual had been *forced* to abdicate and been made a slave of society. Thomas Hobbes (1588–1679)[2] started from this basis to "prove" that, exactly because man had originally been a sovereign creature and still retained a hankering after independence, an ordered society was possible only under a regime of despotic absolutism. More than a hundred years later, Rousseau (1712–1778) won fame and popularity by advocating a return to the "aboriginal state" of nature with its unchecked freedom.

"Man is born free, yet everywhere we find him in chains." With this resounding fanfare Rousseau had opened his *Contrat Social,* which preached that man in his pristine freedom had been the best and noblest of beings and that what had corrupted him was society. Another century later we find these words of Rousseau metamorphosed into the phantasmagoric Marxian gospel of the dissolution of the state by a proletarian revolution, which was to corrode the shackles Rousseau had discovered and leave nothing but footloose primordial man, his "freedom," and a confused state of affairs "in which the free development of each is the condition for the free development of all."

All biological and anthropological evidence brands these men prophets of topsy-turvydom. The case of Karl Marx is particularly illuminating, because his chief philosophic mentor, Hegel, had seen and stated the truth as clearly as one possibly could. Far from identifying freedom with a "golden age," or paradise, which man forfeited through his own fault or some villainy, Hegel,[3] on the contrary, based his whole evolutionary philosophy on one maxim: "The history of the world is nothing but the development of the idea of freedom." He stated this again and again. Yet his disciple Marx completely missed these numerous red-letter passages, or turned them into the opposite.

The question whether man appeared on earth a free and sovereign creature, or whether he began unfree and is seeking freedom, remains of fundamental practical importance and is not merely food for idle speculation. Suppose, to take an analogous case, physicists and engineers had been led to believe by some spellbinder that there was a time when matter was not yet under the curse of gravity, but "free" and able to do anything and fly anywhere. They would have wasted centuries on attempts to exorcise gravity from matter. Fortunately, physical science having since Galileo been guided by wiser counsel than that of the magicians, we can afford to laugh at the idea of matter hexed by gravity.

But we may have been laughing too soon, for our practical problems cannot all be solved by physicists and engineers. They must be solved on the vital plane of human relations, and on this level, alas, the necromancers and magicians are still in power.

ARCHAIC MAN

Anthropological evidence clearly shows that "original man" had not advanced far beyond the state of the animal shackled by its instincts. The most primitive animals are, in a sense, still almost identical with their environment, virtually "water in water." Similarly, the most primitive humans know themselves to be practically identical with, part and parcel of, their environment. They are suspended in a sort of magical chaos of powers embracing the very air about them, the sky, the clouds, the soil with its vegetation and fauna, the wind and the sun, thunder and lightning, and their fellow tribesmen. All these are largely one thing to archaic man and he is part of them as they are part of him, so much so that one part may the next instant transform itself into another. Even the difference between "I" and "You" is hardly known.

This mystic identification of primitive man with the environment involves the identity of individual and tribe. The true primitive is incapable of thinking of himself as of an individual. He is in fact no individual, but merely, as is every animal, a specimen of the species, and the species means no more than his own tribe. All other tribes are imposters, evil spirits which have temporarily assumed human shape. This attitude is still reflected, e.g., in the first article of creed of one of the Dakota tribes: "The Lakotapi are the original people, superior to all others of mankind, and it is a matter of grace on their part to concede rights of any kind to any other people."[4] Such may at one time have been the ideology of cannibalism. But whether it was or not, the same primitive creed survives to this day in every original people, every chosen people, every master race, every religion with the sole means of grace, and every only genuine political dogma. It does not augur well for the freedom and sovereignty of original man.

For us of this day it is virtually impossible to realize the full significance of the spiritual fog of which such creeds were born. But of this we may be certain—life in such circumstances was (and still is) anything but what Laotse, Hobbes, Rousseau and their followers imagined to have been the aboriginal freedom of man, and what Marxism promises to bring back by inducing a "withering away" of the state. So much also seems certain, that whatever consciousness archaic man possessed at first became manifest almost exclusively in *fear*. The summary of such consciousness which the Eskimo shaman gave to Knud Rasmussen is nothing but a litany of tribal fears:

We fear the weather spirit of the earth that we must fight against . . . We fear Takánakapsâluk, the great woman down at the bottom of the sea . . . We fear the sickness that we meet daily all around us . . . We fear the evil spirits of life, those of the air, of the sea and the earth . . . We fear the souls of the dead human beings and of the animals we have killed . . . We fear the sea about us, and we fear all the invisible things that are likewise about us."[5]

Of this kind, generally, is the "freedom" of primitive man. A being of this nature is the last on earth to live for and by himself, "free and independent." Physically and mentally archaic man can survive the unrelenting terror of his environment only because he lacks true individual consciousness, because his consciousness is merged with that of his kindred, is diffuse tribal consciousness.

This state of things is the almost unanimous report from every quarter of the globe where within the last century primitives were still discovered—including those of our own backwoods, rural and industrial, where solidarity, conformity and orthodoxy are the supreme law.

PRIMITIVE RIGIDITY

The confession of the Eskimo shaman points out another typical characteristic of primitivity, its utter inflexibility. "Therefore it is that our fathers have inherited from their fathers all the old rules of life which are based on the experience and the wisdom of generations. We do not know, we cannot say why, but we keep these rules in order that we may live untroubled."[6] The primitive's own way of life is to him the only possible way of life, the only right way of life. He is the most orthodox of all creatures. And though he may realize, as did the Eskimo, that his rules are the rules of ignorance, nevertheless they are rigidly adhered to, since it is better to cling to systematized ignorance than to have nothing to hold on to in this perplexing universe of fear.

All this, in a way, mirrors the physical conditions under which life seems to have originated. The physical environment of the earliest organisms was marked in many regards by great uniformity.

No doubt, life could get a foothold on this planet exactly because the monotony and steadiness of the primordial environment, the sea, proved an ideal incubator. Similarly, the tenacity with which primitive man clings to what fixity and constancy there is must have been an essential condition of human beginnings.

Nowhere, therefore, is change so dreaded as among primitives —because every slightest change may mean a potential upheaval of the very foundations of existence. Nowhere is life so strictly formal, straitjacketed in ceremony, as among archaic men. Ironclad etiquette rules everything; every daily routine, work and war, religious ritual and other ceremonial pomp, the hunting and killing of prey, the preparation of food and drink, the kind of dress to be worn, as well as the making of tools and weapons. There is no domain of life which is not under strict regimentation.

Only inflexible customs, conventions and mores can give the primitive a modicum of security in a bewildering world of flux, danger and fear. But as an animal almost exclusively guided by instinct is not free, neither can social man be free so long as his behavior is guided by customs and precepts as absolute as are the animal's instincts.

How seriously all this is to be taken may best be gathered from the severity of punishment inflicted by all primitives upon the slightest deviation from established custom. There is, as a rule, but one penalty—death, or, what is practically synonymous with it, expulsion into the extratribal world of nature's open terror. There is no place under such conditions for romantic individualism and freedom.

Primitive rigidity has remained a powerful factor far into the historical phase of human evolution. Even the ancient Greeks, the first people among whom individualism became a turbulent social movement, nevertheless harbored among their laws large remnants of primordial fixity.[7] Irrespective of its meritorious elements, Plato's *Republic* remains in some regards the distressing blueprint for a police state of male bluestockings living under ideal blue laws.

While the whole Orient is, of course, an arsenal of archaic
fixtures and social petrifacts, the best-documented case of archaic
rigidity within historic times is furnished by the Hebrews, among
whom law and religion were still one thing, and who regarded the
slightest breach of their primordial rules of life a crime against the
deity, as likely as not punishable by death. "If thou wilt not observe
to do all the words of this law ... the Lord will make thy plagues
wonderful, and the plagues of thy seed, ... and every sickness and
every plague, which is not written in the book of this law, them
will the Lord bring upon thee, until thou be destroyed."[8]

The very notion of freedom under such conditions is an absurd-
ity because, in the words of the (Hindu) law of Manu, "there
would be only confusion in the universe if punishment no longer
held its sway. . . . Punishment alone governs all created beings,
punishment alone protects them, punishment alone watches over
them while they sleep."[9]

Archaic monotony and rigidity show even in physical appearance. As Darwin put it, "If you have seen one Fuegian you have
seen all Fuegians—one Tasmanian, all Tasmanians." And in
psychic traits as well. Strict primitive law, being the dominant
factor of the spiritual environment, always is the paramount means
of social selection. Nonconformists are put to death and only the
stereotyped specimen has a chance to survive. Waitz reported that
the slave trader in Upper Egypt appraised a slave exclusively according to his place of birth, that is, his tribe, "for long experience
has taught him that the differences between individuals of the same
tribe are negligible beside those which are due to race."[10]

Thus, to be fit for human society on the primitive level means
to be a strict totalitarian conformist, to live without even the
notion of freedom, to submit in the smallest and often absurdest
details to rigid unchanging patterns, laws, customs, habits and
superstitions, and to risk the loss of one's life for the slightest
refractoriness.[11] The individual is nothing, the tribe everything.
Wherever this is the case, evolution is slow or impossible because
evolution depends at every stage on the delegation of autonomy

by the whole to individuals or parts. The "living" crystals are the result of the assignment of individual functions to certain atoms or groups of atoms. Coghill[12] has shown that the principle applies throughout biological development. And it holds for social evolution as well.

It is not difficult to imagine, as did thumb-sucking visionaries from Laotse to this day, a hypothetical primordial "state of nature," a paradise in which each individual followed his own whims and inclinations, his own pursuit of happiness and freedom. But no social life would ever have arisen from such a state. The elemental basis of social evolution, the continuity of tradition, would be lacking and definite social patterns be impossible. In fact, even the development of human language would have been impossible. Everything essential to our concept of man would be lacking, and Homo sapiens would have remained Homo silvester, a superior sort of mammal, but an inhuman creature all the same.

The monotony of the primitive social environment with its spiritual tyranny was the sine qua non of early social development because everywhere continuity is the first essential of discontinuity. Yet, if it was necessary, it also represented an often insuperable evolutionary barrier. Rigidity is stagnation. And since mind and body are one, correlates of a single living system, the probability is high that people who have for thousands of years lived in inflexible primitivity, or even an inflexible fossilized civilization, will remain organically and mentally unfit to adapt themselves to freer conditions. For the truth is that, since man is his own chief environmental factor, every social environment becomes a breeding establishment and contains an intrinsic breeding policy, apt to bring forth through selection and elimination a very particular strain, one fit to live only in its own peculiar environment and nowhere else. Freedom and primitivity, then, are incompatible, or nearly so. Wherever rigid custom, law, religious dogma and practice have become as ingrained as instincts, they are liable to become evolutionary barriers as hard to overcome as instincts themselves.

We touch here on a problem which traditional science in its exclusively materialistic orientation has failed to see but which the new scientific dispensation, recognizing only "the ghostly remains of matter," has moved into a glaring light. We are referring to the fact that in the world of man the usual zoological taxonomy based chiefly on dead bones is about as pertinent as would be a theory of art founded on the chemistry of pigments. In other words, biological science has not yet officially recognized man as a mental creature. It still treats him as an interesting lump of that stuff which physics used to call matter but whose very reality now is beset with grave doubts. Differently stated, the suggestion is here made that it would be in closer agreement with the philosophy of the new physics, at least as far as man is concerned, to complement physical taxonomy with mental taxonomy and biological speciation by mental speciation. We shall deal with this subject at some length in Chapter 10. Here it must suffice to point out that the differences between archaic or primitive man and civilized man warrant this point of view. As will become apparent, the entire complex of problems here involved is inseparable from the problem of the instincts. It is in the instinctual domain that the differences between animals and man in general, as well as between archaic man and civilized man, are most striking. To the extent that animals are ruled by instinct in their environmental relations they remain automata leaning toward the dead-end side of evolution. The reason why man alone has largely avoided the danger up to now is that he discovered ways of circumventing mechanistic, instinctual absolutism. This is the secret of human evolution, which sociologists have almost systematically overlooked. We must, therefore, after this brief excursus into anthropology, return to the instincts as the fundamental problem of human, i.e., social, evolution. For, the instincts being the basic regulators of the organism-environment complementarity, the evolutionary history of social man becomes, from the viewpoint of fundamental science, essentially a *sociology of instinct*. All other aspects are of secondary importance.

6

THE PROCESS OF SUBLIMATION

WHEN, straining my mind's eye to peer down the long perspective of time, I try to penetrate the bewildering kaleidoscope of visible forms, what always overwhelms me is that the apparent chaos is really a precious order, the work of one grand creative stroke. Then the hard materiality of things begins to soften, it becomes transparent, lucidly aligned, and in place of the superficial crazy quilt of life I behold a few plain principles, hardly more than you could count on the fingers of one hand. And soon what was visible dissolves into great music, a moving, glittering, stirring wealth of sound based on no more than a few notes, a simple theme, and one or two rules of composition. Then I think I have the secret of it all.

At such moments I am no doubt an optimist and I usually come to with a start. I begin to tell myself that thinking man will forever remain a riddle even to himself, because, all told, even inanimate matter remains no less a mystery than life itself.

Yet again, does the fact that we shall never know the ultimate secret make useless what we do know? I think not. Did life fail to evolve because it did not know what life is? Nor need we know the final secret of life to appreciate important differences between plants and animals and between animals and man. And the fact remains that many of the elements of order science has so far discovered in the world pertain to man as well—meaning that whatever man has gained through evolution he did not achieve by kicking over the traces but by keeping within the laws of nature. We must therefore turn our attention to the fundamentals of sociogenesis.

THE GRAND PERSPECTIVE

Since the beginning of our century a great deal of intensive and often ingenious study has been devoted to animal societies by animal psychologists or ethologists. It may not be out of place here to point out that the terms "ethology" and "ethologist" are formed from the same root as "ethic." This is an indication that ethic in general is at last on the way of becoming part of science. By adopting the name ethology for their science, animal psychologists have (perhaps reluctantly even in some of their factions) acknowledged that an ethos is the quintessence of every order of life. And where the ethos becomes conscious, we have of course what in the human world we call "ethic."

Among scientists there is today not a shade of doubt of there being a continuous, if sometimes jumpy, development from the subatomic stratum to the atomic and the molecular level, from there to the organic, to the sociomental domains of animals and humans, up to the loftiest manifestations of the human spirit. What is of cardinal importance for the purposes of this study is that *basically* human behavior is still animal behavior, more or less modified (in some instances) by intellect and social organization directed by thought. In other words, and in terms of our fundamental concept, even human behavior, though largely raised to the level of consciousness and often extremely complex, is still a matter of *organism-environment complementarity*. Behavior that does not elicit the appropriate response, individually or with regard to the entity of society, remains as wasteful, fruitless, or as damaging as trying to open a door with the wrong key.

The beginnings of all animal societies are instinctive, and some zoologists have classified them, according to the three main instincts, as mating societies, defensive societies and feeding societies. This seems unnecessary to me. It is simpler to look at all of them as mere continuations of a much older "instinct," that of species integration. But if one would single out a particular one among those unifying "trends" most commonly leading to social organization, the mating urge would no doubt prove to be the most important. Even normally completely solitary animals become social in the mating season. This makes the reproductive instinct the primary social instinct. Among higher animals at least there is no reproduction apart from a certain social function.

From this basis all social organization may have developed, even human society. The animal world offers every stage of transition from the casual mating, after which (as with amphibians, reptiles and some primitive birds) the eggs are abandoned to hatch by themselves and whose young are self-supporting from the moment of birth, to the intricate societies of man. Putting in a store of food for the hatching young, even if the parents never live to see them, and personal care of the young are the next steps in family evolution. The latter case may lead to actual marriage (among birds, e.g.), which may last till the brood reaches maturity, or for a few years, or even for a lifetime. There are even (again among birds) formal prenuptial engagements contracted sometimes months before the actual consummation of the marriage. All this is accomplished without the aid of spoken language of the kind man possesses. From the rearing of the young to courtship and mating, from the personal dealings of two individuals to the social understanding of large flocks and herds, all communicative functions are instinctive, achieved by semaphoric and acoustic sign languages, inborn and spontaneous.

But as we shift our observation from the lower to the higher animal kingdom we encounter more and more elements of intelligence, though the gap between even the most evolved apes and the least developed of men remains enormous. We can perhaps best sum up the problem this way: animals are caught in a vicious instinctual circle. Man has broken out of this circle and expanded into a world infinitely richer, greater, freer. What was the secret which permitted it? We have already hinted at the answer. Again we are confronted with a new phase in an established trend, a further extension of complementarity to new frontiers.

The earliest forms of life, we saw, established the principle between the single cell and the environment. Multicellular organisms expanded it to embrace countless cells on the organismal side. Man and other social creatures extended it still further to include countless creatures on the environmental side, which is as great an evolutionary leap as that from a microbe to a mouse. But this still leaves out of account the startling differences between such complex animal societies as those of some insects and those of man. The difference is crucial and demands at least brief consideration.

In 1911 the great Harvard entomologist William Morton Wheeler[1] showed that an ant colony can be understood only if regarded as a single physiological unit. Its alimentary system is common to all; it has, in Forel's phrase, "a social stomach." Whatever nourishment an individual ant swallows will ultimately have been swallowed by the whole colony, because it circulates by way of the exchange of regurgitations. The ant society also possesses a common glandular system, in which hormones and other regulator substances are distributed by means of mutual licking and grooming. These and certain hereditary factors controlled by the queen are the colony's social organizers. *All insect societies are purely physiological societies,*[2] generally consisting of a mother and her offspring, and thus have not significantly advanced beyond the organizational status of multicellular animals, which also represent physiologically integrated descendants of a single maternal cell.

Beyond doubt, human societies arose from the same base, the family, as is evident in all primitive tribes, still founded on genealogical relationships, blood bonds. Our civilizations, however, have discarded physiological organization for something with far richer possibilities. *Their novel organizer is the conscious mind.*

Herein lies the true revolutionary character of man. Not, as is generally said, in the mere fact that he *has* mind, intelligence (animals, too, have it, though to a lesser degree), but that *he uses it to supplant physiological means of regulating interindividual relations,* for purposes of *species integration on the multi-individual level.* Unless we fully grasp the truly revolutionary meaning of this step, i.e., the radical difference in organizational methods between insect ·societies and man, we shall never understand the unique evolutionary position of man.

Yet, no matter how great may appear the gap between the purely physiological organization in insect societies and mental organization in human civilization, the *principle* of organization is always the same. We might speak of a change in organizational media, but the principle is never other than integrative complementarity, which, on the levels of life above the unicellular creatures, always means *species integration,* either multicellular or multi-individual. Which suggests that perhaps even the organizational media may be merely increasingly complex variations on a fundamental theme, and their differences possibly mere differences in degree and not in kind. In other words, thought and mind are perhaps not such radical innovations as a superficial glance might lead us to believe.

THE GENESIS OF THOUGHT

Mind, it has been suggested, did not appear in man unheralded, but doubtless is as old as life, in part synonymous with it, for both "life" and "mind" are terms having reference to the organism-environment complementarity. But according to the view now held by many leading physicists, even life might not be the beginning of mind. On the contrary, mind appears to be the beginning of everything. In Eddington's[3] famous formulation, "the stuff of the world is mind-stuff." The conviction now gaining ground among the vanguard of physicists is that all existence is the "actualization" of relations, i.e., of mental (metaphysical) constructs; and only because the foundation of the world is mental can scientists at all formulate the simplest physical manifestations by means of such mental operations as mathematics. It takes mind to understand mind and mind can comprehend nothing but mind.

We have previously defined *thought* as the *conscious formulation* of relations, whereas the physicists' "actualization" of relations would necessarily be unconscious. These two types of mind have long been familiar, and Bohr himself drew attention to their complementary nature. The evolutionary significance of this cannot be overlooked. Whatever mind plants and the lower animal orders may possess is innate mostly in their relatively passive *chemo-physiology*. With the highest vertebrates, especially man, increasing mental consciousness and active thought depend on the *electro-physiology* of the supreme exponent of animality, the neurocerebral system. The evolutionary process apparent here seems based on a shift from vegetative-protonic to dynamic-electronic dominance.

The transition, of course, is gradual. Only with man, in human societies organized by thought, does the dynamic electronic-animalic principle finally reach for its zenith. It was the gradual shift of emphasis from the protonic to the electronic aspect of the fundamental complementarity that provided the revolutionary impact of thought and raised consciousness to a much higher power than the essentially vegetative levels permitted. With man, the *animal par excellence* appeared on earth, and conscious thought was born, delivered from the intrauterine nurture of dormant vegetativeness into the light of day.

But, be it stressed once more, as birth is no absolute beginning out of nothing, neither can conscious thought be such in evolution. If thought is the conscious formulation of relations, even unconscious mind, even "mind that is mere matter," still remains the "actualization" of relations. Relatedness is everything. Being means expressing relationships. And the more intense and organized the relations are, the more their mental nature becomes apparent. Hence, as soon as, in evolution, molecular patterns reach the complexity of a cell depending on the continuous interaction between itself and the environment, possibly affecting even the subatomic stratum, the "mental construct" (again to use the language of physicists) underlying the situation becomes manifest as life, which no doubt always means a degree of awareness of the organism-environment relations. The behavior of many protozoans is not too different from that of some much higher ranking metazoans. Even they can learn, and learning bespeaks mind; mind, probably, which on this level is not yet thought, but which in the course of evolution could reach the stage of thought, as it does in the ontogeny of most normal human embryos.

That there is even instinctive abstract logic is proved by the "language" of the honeybees, which Karl von Frisch[4] succeeded in "decoding." Nothing could be more logical than the way the scouts communicate to the field workers the spatial relationships of hive, sun and newly located sources of nectar—in dances which seem to have derived their rules from the surveyor's rules of triangulation. Still, though this *is* a language of logical formulation, a very specific form of intelligence, it remains instinctive; the bees are born with it and do not have to learn it.

Instinct in general is one of thought's precursors. It is inborn hereditary thought, formulating the animal's relations to the environment in standardized patterns of behavior; thought, one might say, which, like the Mexican newt Axolotl, proved itself so efficient in immature form, it saw no reason at all to aspire to adulthood.

Human thought, then, may also be looked upon as the sublime offspring of instinct, the result of a fission of an original simple unit into a complementary pair, concomitant with the transmutation of an offshoot of the primitive olfactory lobe into the conscious cerebral cortex. But as even in man part of the old instinctive brain is maintained in the phylogenetically oldest cerebral region, so also instinct itself retains some of its old functions in their own proper spheres.

This brings us to the all-important question: what, in the world of man, was the role which instinct played in the process we called species integration, that is, in sociogenesis? The question is so fundamental it requires detailed consideration.

THE REPRODUCTIVE INSTINCT

We have seen that life is synonymous with consciousness, however inchoate, and identical with the expansion of the primal organizational principle over the relationships of a physical system and its environment. Novel qualitative aspects of physical systems, as we observe them in life and consciousness, are often designated as "emergents" of the evolutionary process, and they appear whenever a new threshold is crossed, with every extension of the principle of complementarity into a higher sphere of environmental relationships. Since all such relationships fundamentally are governed by instinct, it is to be expected that even on the highest levels of life, such as the social organizations of man, which also rest on environmental interdependences, the basic instincts determine many of the emergents specific of social evolution.

Now instinct may, as we said before, be regarded as a special, or limiting, case of intelligence, an inborn, hereditary form of thought. The widening of the instinctual sphere, therefore, as it becomes apparent in social integration, is always accompanied by a corresponding expansion, or transformation, of the psychic domain. Freud appropriately called this the *sublimation* of instinct. But whatever name we give it, the cardinal point to be borne in mind is that it is the result of the extension of complementary relationships from the purely organic to the social sphere. Social scientists subsume the entire complex of emergents associated with this evolutionary stride under the term *culture*.

In order to follow this process in the reproductive field, let us consider the origin of a feline family. A polarity arises between female and male which in the mating is forthwith "short-circuited." The partners cease to be of interest to one another and go their separate ways. However, as in the case of the amoeba swallowing a particle of food, so here again the "short circuit" is not a real annihilation of the initial field, but its conversion into a series of internal physiological processes—fertilization and gestation. Throughout the latter, mother animal and unborn young constitute a single physiological field. Nor is the situation radically altered with the birth of the kittens, since these still depend on the mother. The field of the primary social instinct thus becomes enlarged into a social pattern of longer duration, a family. That is to say, one arc of the reproductive circuit has become socially *institutionalized* and at the same time now serves other environmental concerns, the food instinct and the defensive instinct. Of utmost importance, however, is this: whereas the mating act, the primary social function, is entirely determined by instinct, its outcome, the family, already evinces a measure of intelligence and perhaps even of quasi-ethical qualities, as may be inferred from the aura of affection and the way the cat defends and educates her young. The sublimation of raw instinct, that is, its partial conversion into mental values, is thus coupled to the widening of a multicellular into a multi-individual or social system. Conscious mind is given its great evolutionary chance as soon as circumstances arise in which physiological methods of regulating a social system begin to fail.

The institution of the normal animal family too is of relatively short duration. It dissolves as soon as the young come under the sway of sexual impulses, just about the time when the mother cat herself enters a new reproductive phase. The primary social instinct disrupts the secondary social pattern, the family. Instinctive concerns have been somewhat enlarged and temporarily have linked together a number of individuals, but the vicious circle of the instincts is not yet broken, and the social system never grows beyond the bounds of the provisional family.

Today it is beyond doubt that ages and ages ago the same situation was also typical of man's ancestors. In the great majority of human branches, however, two significant developments took place, neither of them exclusively human, but in their combination not found elsewhere in the mammalian world. First, the family came to be maintained beyond the reproductive maturity of the young. Second, the male of the species himself was finally made part of the family.

Consider first what were the consequences of the inclusion of the third generation into the social pattern. For simplicity's sake, let us assume this genealogical society to consist of a grandmother and her four daughters, each of these with four children of her own. If we tried to reduce the situation to a diagram we would get a constellation of 21 random points, each connected with all others by double lines representing mutual relations—110 links in all, or a fairly dense filigree.

But even this would not furnish the remotest suggestion of what is really involved. Doubtless, what enables primitive humans to maintain a three-generation family is brains ranking much higher than a cat's. The problem thus becomes one of interplay between 21 times 10 billion brain cells. Even if we assume that at any time less than half of these become involved, how many "hook-ups" are possible between 100 billion cells? The figure would fill many times the number of books in the world! Add to this that each brain cell contains perhaps more electrons than there are suns in our galaxy, and you get a feeble suggestion of how out of such cerebral complexity can arise the miracle of creative thought, of reason, of ethical concepts, of language, and the thousand other manifestations of human life. Somewhere in this potentiation of functional brain circuits within a social system a threshold was crossed, above which a difference of degree became a difference of kind and exalted man far above the animal kingdom.

The cardinal point then to be kept in mind is that all this became possible only after one aspect of the reproductive instinct had become institutionalized in the family based on complementary relationships. This is one side of the sublimation of the sexual instinct.

Of equal importance may be another reproductive factor. The human infant is by all mammalian standards born eleven months prematurely.[5] It reaches a stage of development that mammals of comparable rank and size attain at birth only toward the end of its first postnatal year. Instead of completing its ontogeny in intra-uterine isolation, it has been given the opportunity to complete more than half of it in an open social world. The singular development of the human brain thus made possible therefore is the result, no longer of inherited predisposition and the rigid determinism of the past, but of the conscious experience of organism-environment interaction with its correlate of freedom. Thus the brain, thanks to the "physiologically normalized premature birth," develops into a *social brain*, much less instinct-tied, less mechanical, more adaptable than the normal animal brain and exceptionally well-suited to make the most of environmental complementarities.

Moreover, premature birth put a premium on parental care, i.e., "social intelligence," favoring the survival of those with better brains. Certain it is that with the first appearance of man the most important evolutionary problems became social problems. Even earliest man must have begun to realize that fulfillment lay no longer in "nature" at large but in his own kind. The gods, spirits and totemic ancestors which his mind created are symbols of the new universe which had been opened to him through the integration of successive generations. His very brain is the result of social feedbacks, as the further social evolution is the manifestation of growing brain power. The human mind, therefore, is anything but Teilhard de Chardin's naïve total of all brain cells, not a matter of *additivité dirigée*,[6] but of progressive cerebral *integration* within the primitive group.

The second significant difference which sets off human families from those of most animals is the integration of the male. Except for a few species of apes, the male is never a member of the mammalian family, and with the latter he is but sire and defender, no more. But in the normal human family he is provider as well, and this complete instinctual integration, apparent in monogamous marriage, brought forth phenomena the likes of which we find nowhere else, an enlargement and enrichment of the social field which can hardly be overestimated.

Throughout most of the animal kingdom the reproductive polarity exhausts itself in casual and sporadic "short circuits." In every short circuit a store of energy is dissipated in a spark or flash, after which the system is dead. But if polarity is made to operate through complex installations tempering its vehemence, if it has to carry a load, the system can be maintained indefinitely and become productive.

Something of this nature took place in the world of man when, possibly long after the societies of mothers and children had been established, the males became permanently integrated. So long as the reproductive instinct remained divorced from the social environment, it could not but mean a most disturbing periodic tension, and therefore a factor of social disequilibration, a relapse into sheer unmitigated animality.[7]

Compared with this state of things, the maintenance of permanent relations between reproductive partners constituted an enrichment of the social field beyond measure. Instead of periodic tense fields short-circuiting themselves, there now prevailed an atmosphere of ease and relaxation, which enormously enlarged the mind's scope of free play, freed an unsuspected store of energies which now could become socially creative, and thus permitted the development of the social nucleus far beyond the purely mammalian family.

But there are still deeper aspects to this event. The adult male being in many respects totally different from the female, whereas the purely mammalian family of females and immature males was essentially all-female, the incorporation of the adult male carried into the social milieu the whole unfathomable mystery of asymmetric complementarity. On a much higher level this takes us back to our fundamental theme. True complementarity is never possible between equals. And though in an essentially female family there are still the differences due to age, among adult women of a primitive nature the divergences are negligible and potentials therefore lacking. The incorporation of the adult male hence meant a fundamental complementarity permanently institutionalized, and therefore a decisive evolutionary stride, comparable to the genesis of atoms through the integration of protons and electrons, or the origin of the first "living crystals" in asymmetric molecular patterns. *"C'est la dissimétrie qui crée le phénomène,"* said Pierre Curie.[8]

Only now, with the integration of the male into the family, was the foundation laid for an "explosive" social development, which began with the etherealization of the second side of the reproductive instinct. Only to a man united to a woman beyond the reproductive act could his sexual complement reveal qualities never before suspected, qualities not part of sheer animalic sex: a mind, a soul, beauty and human warmth. None but lasting social ties could ever bring about the sublimation of instinct into phenomena of the mind and this alone could start primitive man on the way to true humanity.

The human mind, creative thought, could emerge only in a social milieu because, being itself the consciousness of relations, it needed an open environment of intensified relationships in order fully to awaken. Where there are no relations, thought has nothing to "cut its teeth on." Part of this process of human beginnings is the sublimation of animal instinct into conscious conduct, the ethical ordering of social relations (which among insects are still governed by physiological factors).

THE ALIMENTARY INSTINCT

In the matter of food, man does not stand alone in having raised instinct to a social concern. Many animals have achieved that. But, here again, what makes man unique is that, by involving instinct into conscious cortical functions on a vast superindividual scale, he brought his alimentary concerns to a high degree of sublimation and thus induced the emergence of phenomena for which we would search in vain in the rest of the animal kingdom.

It can hardly be doubted that man himself once fed like an animal, for there are still primitives in our midst who have not yet outgrown animal behavior in front of a food pile, though they may somehow have acquired silver spoons and elegant dinner plates.

What is animal behavior in the alimentary field?

An illuminating example was reported to me by a distant in-law. A good many years ago this man and his wife arrived in Naples as the sole passengers of a small freighter, and on disembarking had to go in search of a porter. They finally found one soundly asleep in a shady corner. On being awakened and asked to help the travelers with their baggage, the Neapolitan, however, answered with but a declining gesture and an apathetic *Ho già mangiato*— I've eaten already.

Here we have characteristic animal behavior. There is no thought of the future, not even the future lying but a few hours ahead. But when hunger awakens, the animal and the primitive become hunger incarnate. The whole world then narrows down to a tortuous tunnel through which, oblivious of everything else, the creature strives toward its next meal, which, when gulped down, again annihilates the food field. Again the creature is without concerns, "free" to withdraw within itself, free to sleep, free not to be alive.

It was a significant departure from this animalism when man— more likely it was woman—began to take thought of the future, and the perpetual series of alimentary "short circuits" gave way to a preoccupation with food as a permanent problem, best solved by systematic food production. It is well to draw attention to the fact that the only animal societies that have attained food production—ants, termites and bees—are essentially female societies. The nursing sex, as Wheeler pointed out, has much greater need of forethought than has the male. In the world of man, too, we have every reason to believe that the change from food gathering and hunting to systematic food production is an extension of the nursing instinct, for in many primitive societies field work is still the business of the women and beneath the dignity of the semi-domesticated males.

But we are here chiefly dealing with the emergence in the food field of those mental characteristics which brought about the full humanization of primitives and widened the scope of man's freedom. As was already mentioned, it would be a mistake to attribute to man a monopoly of such traits; in an inchoate form we find them in many animals, but *never* outside a social milieu, of which they are in the truest sense the efflorescences. Man, however, could go infinitely further than any animal.

Gustav Bally,[9] to whom we have already referred, has shown how in the world of man every animal instinct brings forth a way of life characteristic of the social stratum in which it becomes embodied, and that animal *behavior* always becomes enhanced into social *conduct*, that is, an *ethical* attitude. In the alimentary field this is manifest in those moral attributes we call diligence, a conservative spirit, and the "economic attitude" in general.

It is of interest in this connection, because it brings out the great evolutionary lines, to draw attention to the fact that the food instinct belongs to the vegetative side of animalism, and that we can trace the economic or conservative "attitude" through the vegetative systems of animals, the plant kingdom and inert matter, down to the protons. All these are either food-producing systems or conservatories of the world's energies. But only in social man has this long evolutionary line emerged into full consciousness. In him alone has economic activity surmounted pure instinct, become regulated by thought, and expanded into a life beyond survey. Thus another instinct became institutionalized in the social sphere, first in agriculture, and later in all other economic activity developing from it.

But this process should not be considered in the first place in its material aspects; the mental ones are primary. Only because man, thanks to his social brain, arrived at a considered "manner of handling" the food problem did he acquire manners in general. It was the art of doing the right thing at the right time, so important in agriculture, which gradually engrossed his sense of what is fitting, which, translated into the realities of social intercourse, meant nothing less than the acquisition of tact, propriety. Even the palpable manifestations of economic civilizations became possible only because the sublimation of raw instinct meant in the first place the rise of a conscious ethos, now generally referred to as honesty or integrity in the business world.

An immense part of material and spiritual civilization thus is the direct or indirect consequence of the "socialization" of the alimentary instinct through the partial displacement of once automatic processes by conscious cerebral functions, rational and ethical. Spontaneous physiological economy enlarged into social economy directed by thought. And though we may readily admit that our economic systems are still heavily imbued with brute animal motives, the organization of our economic life is nonetheless the work of the conscious mind, not, as among insects, of chemo-physiological factors.

Only social integration offered biological evolution the chance to overcome its own limits, because only the intensive development of complementary relationships in a social field made it possible to involve the cerebral cortex in functions once purely instinctive and to sublimate these into social values. Probably no other way would have led to the freedom that man gained through this process.

THE DEFENSIVE INSTINCT

Defense, too, when raised to a social concern in man's world and removed from the purely physiological domain, manifests a rational and an ethical aspect. It is not without interest that human reason has usually been taken for granted among the evolutionists, whereas ethics has long been their Cinderella, perhaps because, as Dobzhansky[10] suggests, all previous "attempts to discover a biological basis of ethics suffer from mechanistic oversimplification." Since we have constantly referred to the topic in this chapter, we can no longer evade the question: what is ethics?

We all know the pragmatic answer. But what would be an

answer acceptable to evolutionary theory? It would seem that, if "the stuff of the world is mind-stuff," ethics as an aspect of the human mind must likewise have its roots in the basic "mind-stuff." And if it means drawing the last practical conclusions from the evolutionary truth that no being is self-sufficient but dependent on countless others, we are probably justified in calling ethics the conscious or unconscious recognition of complementarity as the very essence of existence. Conversely, this makes complementary interdependence also the fundamental proposition of ethics, its most elemental form. No wonder ethics cannot be derived from biology! It now appears as the highest sublimation in a long periodic series reaching back to the beginning of things.

Let us see now what are its manifestations on the dynamic side of the instinct of self-preservation, defense. Whereas the chief functions of vegetative systems in all evolution are the accumulation of energies and surpluses, the production of goods and their distribution, dynamic systems are never materially productive. Their essence is, as Bergson said, the "discontinuous and explosive" spending of reserves. This certainly is true also of human military systems. Yet it should not make us overlook their positive contributions to evolution. By its very nature, which is animalic-dynamic, the way of life of the warrior was bound to bring forth ethical concepts and an ethical attitude different from those of vegetative economic man. Much more than with the latter, the life of the soldier, especially the novice, is still dominated by the one overwhelming experience of primitive man: fear. He lives closer to the raw realities of the struggle for existence, and his first impulse in face of an enemy usually is to flee.

But the soldier, in order to become an asset to his people, had to learn to overcome fear, to convert a negative reaction into a positive social constant, a stabilizing factor. He had to acquire a will and the *discipline* to face danger unflinchingly, a determination to risk his life, not for personal advantages, but for the security of the larger body of which he was a part. Thus again, instinctive animal behavior, in the entirely novel social environment dominated by conscious thought, became sublimated into an ethical attitude, into *courage*. The soldier's relations to the body social came to be borne by a sense of *loyalty*, which the latter reciprocated by a sense of *trust*.

The virtues emerging from the defensive sphere are in many regards superior to the values evolved in the alimentary domain. Dynamic timing, the precise adjustment of motion to motion, always vital in single combat as well as in tactical operations, fostered a feeling for mechanism and led to the invention of superior tools. Many of the earliest machines were war machines: the catapult, the battering ram, the horse-drawn chariot, etc. Dynamic timing required greater sensitivity for what is fitting than is needed in the more passive economic life, that is to say, a keener sense of tact. This, together with the self-discipline demanded of the soldier, evinced manners still more refined than those of economic man. For centuries and millennia, indeed, there were no better manners than those of the professional warrior, the nobleman. And if wars were not always fought for the noblest of purposes, soldiers still had imagination enough to endow them with an aura of glory which reflected back on them. It is not by accident that the earliest great poetry was inspired by warlike ventures, never by the grubbing life of agriculture and trade.

Moreover, and again in contrast to the still predominantly self-centered activities of economic life, the virtues of the true soldier are not selfish. His motto is *service*. The very concept of service was born of the warrior class, and the economic stratum even of our late day has been trailing far behind in this regard.

As to the soldier's contributions to human freedom, they are fairly obvious. An enemy conquered or repelled meant a widening of the space-time of relaxed security. The field of play, the scope of free play of the human mind, which depends on a protected social environment, became markedly enlarged. Another division of what on the biological level was the instinct of self-preservation in its mental transmutation became institutionalized in a tangible and permanent organ of the social sphere. And here, too, the gain was one in freedom.

FURTHER SUBLIMATIONS

Summing up what has so far been discussed in this chapter, we can say that the early phase of the emergence of man from the general animal kingdom was still part of biological evolution, for intelligence, consciousness and rudimentary thought are all to be found among the higher animals. But the specifically human enlargement of the mental sphere belongs to a new, social evolution superimposed on the organic. Its newness, that which gives it the stamp of something entirely different in kind, arose largely through what Freud called the process of sublimation, whereby an organic-instinctual substratum gave rise to rational and ethical values and to functions having neither biological antecedents nor narrow biological purposes. This "new evolution" finally resulted in a quasi-autonomy of the mind and the unique ability to communicate mental experiences, to transmit abstract learning from person to person and from generation to generation, even, in the end, across centuries and millennia. All this is part of human freedom.

The mind, though, is not independent of its biological substratum. To a considerable degree it is indeed genetically determined, and certainly in the beginning of human history it could exercise its faculties only on genetically given data. It never had the power consciously to modify anatomy and physiology, though it did discover the possibility to reshape and remold, to imbue with a new spirit the *manifestations* of instinct and so to transform them as to turn them into constructive, creative factors in the nascent social world, which they might easily have thwarted. It is a highly complex process already presupposing at least the initial phases of social evolution, and it may have begun with what Julian Huxley called *ritualization*. The most lucid examples of this are to be found in the transmutation of originally aggressive motions into merely symbolic gestures with an entirely new meaning, even one directly contrary to aggression.

If this was the actual course of development, as the investigations of K. Lorenz[11] and others have made highly probable, then even the instincts underwent a process of self-differentiation (similar to that of so many organs), branching out into two or more mechanisms of which some, or all, attained autonomy. And since the mind as man knows it is, above all, a realized social potential, and society as such possesses no instincts, the various symbolic functions "sublimated" out of instinct could with relative ease enlarge into a mental life far removed from purely biological concerns. In the case of primitive art, religion and various ceremonials, the bond with ritualized instinct is still quite obvious, while such later developments as scholarship and science have become truly autonomous.

The point, then, which we must never forget, is that all these cultural phenomena, and the brain that mediates them, are in the most literal sense *the gifts of society*, conceivable only as concomitants of social organization. Not long ago such a statement would have been declared invalid by most biologists. Geneticists especially maintained the position that the environment never has any influence on heredity. But their views are changing. In the words of Dobzhansky,[12] "It is important to realize that biological heredity and culture, the inborn and the learned behavior, are not independent or isolated entities. They are interacting processes." The social environment has determined a vast amount of human anatomy—neural, muscular and skeletal—even the changes permitting habitual upright posture, for example, in which the relational nature of life and the fact that all vital human situations are face-to-face and heart-to-heart affairs found its fullest physical expression.

So thoroughly integrated are heredity and culture that a hereditary trait now may need the social environment in order to attain its full development. Language presents us with such a case. It is perhaps the most remarkable sublimation of something which in the animal world has an instinctual basis. All animals "speak" in instinctual sign languages, which they do not have to learn. Man speaks in abstract symbols, in words with conventional meanings, and language has become the instrument par excellence for the thoughtful regulation of social functions. Man's language is inseparable from thought and unimaginable in a nonsocial world. It, too, is a gift of society. Yet, though a strictly social phenomenon, the ability to speak in learned abstract symbols has—even if indirectly—become part of the biological heritage of man and is embodied in certain neuromuscular and neurocerebral divisions of anatomy.

But not alone is speech the fruit of social life—it still needs the "spark" of the social environment to be awakened and trained. Where the environment is lacking at the proper time, the hereditary faculty remains undeveloped. This happens in the extremely rare cases of "wild" or "wolf" children, abandoned infants who miraculously survived a thousand vicissitudes, were perhaps suckled by wild animals and later learned to maintain themselves like beasts. If they are brought back to human society not later than their early teens, there is still a chance that they will learn to speak. But if this critical time is missed, such children remain little more than domesticated animals, speechless and unthinking.

This is perhaps the most impressive revelation of the fact that the individual, despite all genetically transmitted traits, has no chance to become human outside the social environment. Humanity is the result of the new evolution much more than of the old, and by reason of being preeminently a social evolution, the new evolution, epitomized in the process of sublimation, is bound to be as much ethical in nature as purely rational.

7

ANIMAL SPECTERS IN THE HUMAN WORLD

W E must here come back once more to Eddington's "great bifurcation" between the inert and the vital branch of the tree of existence. Since instinct is based on physiological mechanisms, there exists between these and the social ethos a relationship closely akin to that between mechanical and organic systems or, to use a different terminology, between rational and irrational ones.

The rational mind is more closely allied with the individual as a biological entity than with the social field, and for this reason more intimately connected with the individual's biological concerns than with the social ethos. This inevitably made the sublimation of instinct a slow and painful process, a continual conflict of interest between animalic-individual leanings and human, i.e., social, demands. In brief, though it *is* the conscious mind which functions as the actual organizer in the new evolution, the mind still merely organizes and manages domains preempted by instinct, claims, as it were, staked out by vested animal interests. The instincts, indispensable as they are, have always proved the greatest subversive force in social evolution.

A further peril arises from the circumstance that the very nature of instinct is tension between an animal and an environmental object, tension that seeks to annul itself in "short circuits." The instincts, therefore, still function according to the elemental least-action principle of physics and this, even if they are not actually destructive, at least "prevents further action" and easily inhibits the enlargement of the social field, impedes the new, psychosocial, evolution.

Every civilization thus rests, as it were, on the powder keg of animal instinct, and it is not surprising that none has lasted too long. The questions, therefore, force themselves on us, (1) whether rational thought is really a free agent or merely the hireling of the instincts; (2) whether a constructive modus vivendi is at all possible between the two, one that would produce more lasting results than civilizations have so far shown and greater freedom.

Before we can attempt to offer answers we must look deeper into the problems they entail.

THE REVOLT OF THE INSTINCTS

Because animal instincts are the chief agents maintaining the equilibrium of the dynamic organism-environment complementarity, they are by their very nature one of the fundamental continuities underlying evolutionary discontinuities. All the various organs and organ systems, which on all levels of evolution arise as embodiments of these environmental relations, lie therefore within the domain of one of the instincts. Here we can only sketchily indicate beginnings and ends of the most important of these evolutionary sequences.

On the vegetative side of self-preservation we have the series of alimentary organs, from the less-than-ephemeral food vacuole of the amoeba to the intricate digestive and circulatory systems of the vertebrates, and the agricultural systems of man. On the animalic-dynamic side of self-preservation a similar sequence leads from the defenselessness of the most primitive cells to a variety of defensive organs, and even chemical warfare in some phyla, to soldier castes among social insects and man's military institutions. In the domain of species preservation, or reproduction, evolution proceeds from mere cell fission, over conjugation and seasonal reproductive organs to permanent sexual organs, to temporary and permanent families, tribes and nations.

To see such series merely as built upon analogy is missing the main point: that they are ever more complex evolutionary variations on one theme. All are systems in which instinct has become institutionalized. Even where, as in the cultural world of man, the systems themselves are no longer of a physiological order but devised and regulated by the conscious mind, the prime moving force in them is still instinct.

Nowhere is this more strikingly apparent than in human rituals, which among primitives still completely dominate social life and every daily activity; they are in fact, almost the only cultural life known to primitives. All these rituals are glorifications of the instincts, and there are no ancient rituals save those celebrating the instincts. The beginning of the new evolution was virtually identical with the rising to full consciousness of instinctual needs, and the mind, therefore, had hardly any other subject to work on.

The reproductive instinct dictates the marriage rites, the initiation mysteries at puberty, circumcision, the worship of the Great Mother or priapic deities, and similar practices. The food instinct is manifest in fertility rites, the magic of rainmaking, the blessing of herds, of seeds and springs, in hunting rites, the conjuring of animals, in many taboos, in burnt offerings and harvest festivals. And finally, war dances, exorcist ceremonies, the blessing of arms, the magic of murder by action-at-a-distance, the placating and bribing of gods and demons by frequent gifts, by fasts and self-inflicted tortures: all these are defensive and protective rituals. Observe almost any such rite, primitive or civilized, and you discover the dictates of elemental urges. So powerful indeed are they that not even the dead are exempt from their tyranny. Burial ceremonies are needed to assure men ample food in afterlife, protection against the sinister spirits which they are bound to meet in the great dark beyond, or their safe arrival at one of the celestial tenements, where, finally, they will be relieved of all molestations of instinct—and where, therefore, deprived of what is most elemental in them, they cannot imagine what they will do with themselves.

This all continues into the highest civilizations, sometimes in subtle form, but just as often not. Thought may organize and manage domains founded on instinct and by instinct, but instinct still "owns" them. Herein lies the germ of the abysmal conflict that is human life: the animal in man resenting mind, the bundles of raw instinct inveighing—even in the name of God and heaven —against the spirit. Freedom, above all evolutionary freedom, therefore is constantly endangered, and we are paying through the nose for having brain enough socially to organize instinctual domains, but not enough really to master our animal propensities. We are all suffering from, and inhibited by, an Instinct Fixation. Something in us resents that we have turned into thinking creatures, and we lean toward perpetual cohabitation with the instincts. This is the core of the tragedy which so far has befallen and destroyed almost every single civilization of which we have any knowledge. Not even we, with all our occasional pride of mind, have really broken the vicious circle of the instincts; we have merely widened it, and in so doing have given instinct more formidable scope than it ever had.

International politics is probably the most obvious instance one can supply, but the national varieties are hardly of a superior nature. Politics is, and has always been, the war of conflicting animal proclivities, no matter in what pious disguise. But even domains in which pure abstract thought has soared to unprecedented heights fare little better. The atomic bomb was not invented as a monument to the sublimity of human thought. Radio and television, two of the most brilliant inventions, have fallen into bondage and are now largely captive workers in the cult of asininity, moronism and the lowest appetites. Here we have the revolt of instinct at its most shocking

Am I disparaging the instincts? No, I am affirming them, if for no other reason than that we cannot live without them. But let us not forget that, as "brain"—the analogue of which every animal possesses—in man's world has come to mean not a mere reflex center but the power of thought, even so man's instincts can serve truly human purposes only if similarly transubstantiated. To some extent, of course, they have been transmuted, at least within the most personal or narrowest social spheres. Beyond these, however, sublimation virtually stops and crude instinct asserts itself. Observe two lovers going hand in hand and wearing a common halo. Instinct? Certainly. Yet more than mere animal instinct. But refer to such a sight where three or four men are gathered, and it is at once pulled down to the level of two beetles mating in the mud. It takes what must almost be called the rigmarole of ritual to keep the revolt of massed instinct from thwarting instinct etherealized. Here lies one of the great problems of evolution.

TENSION AND PLAY

The second crucial problem is rooted in the circumstance that on the lower levels of life instinct manifests itself in high tension seeking to annul itself in "short circuits." Wherever these prevail in the world of man, they must be regarded as vestiges of pure animalism and a threat to man's kingdom.

In Chapter 4 we have shown how, in the animal world, a tense field bears no better fruit than automatic performances, reflex actions, whereas in a field free of tension there is scope for play, for invention, and the variation of otherwise rigid hereditary patterns of behavior. The chimpanzee Sultan could display sparks of intelligence only when he was free from instinctual pull because the playing creature has at least temporarily thrown off part of its animal self. It is, contrary to lower norms, very much alive when its instincts are dormant, and it can be alive because only then is its mind fully awake, whereas, unfailingly, the resurgence of instinct throws the switch which reduces an open mental system to an automaton receptive only to a narrow "band" of physiological stimuli.

The importance of all this for the social world of man can

hardly be overestimated. As the conscious mind built social institutions based on instinctual needs, man transferred some of his
environmental concerns to the social whole and thereby freed
himself of part of his narrow animal self. The virtually closed
circuit, within which the automatic mechanisms of instinct work,
became thereby a *permanently open system,* that is, one no longer
completely self-centered. The results of social organization therefore are not mere fortuitous accidents. They ensue from that basic
law of nature which assures all open systems greater universality
than closed systems, that same law which also made the organic
world, though still a physical world, so vastly different from inert
matter. The prehuman ancestors of man, knowing open minds
only at infrequent moments of abated instinctual promptings,
could become creatures of permanently open minds only through
extensive and intensive social integration.

The human who is all self, pure and unmitigated, is therefore
no longer fit for society; he is an atavistic maniac. Unfortunately,
there exist in every society bodies of such atavists who have discovered that instinct can be organized for its own sake. Most
frequent in the economic sphere, throughout history they often
had their hands in government. Indeed, governmental parasitism
can become a sanctioned tradition, which even we have not completely eradicated. The social world of man, however, having
abandoned physiological organization in favor of integration by
means of thought, demands as its prerequisite the constructive
play of cerebral functions unhampered by instinctual sabotage and
tension. The social atavists generally refute this new evolution;
they still claim the "sacred right" to give free rein to their animal
natures.

Again and again, therefore, it must be stressed that, as in the
animal world, so in the world of man the sine qua non of creative
freedom is conditions of relative ease and the avoidance of instinctual short circuits. And always, the first symptom of freedom
in the world of the living is play. "When the cat is away the mice
will play." Wild animals and the lowest primitive humans, though,

as a rule know play only before maturity. Upon entering adulthood, their protective environment, the family, dissolves, and the experimental freedom of the young capitulates before the absolutism of hereditary behavior or rigid convention. The open, mobile evolutionary frontier of youth then closes down to a few narrow "instinct tunnels." Brothers and sisters of a brood become sexual objects to each other or rivals for the same sexual objects and the same food supply. This always spells the end of social evolution.

On the other hand, where the institution of the family extends beyond two or three generations, the young, on reaching maturity, are able to enter a world still open and offering scope for play. Thus is preserved, often throughout life, the ability to vary living patterns, and to keep cast off the stringencies of inherited mechanisms. This capacity to continue beyond the age of puberty the diversified intellectual curiosity of childhood, a broad interest in things not related to food, sex and defense, is what distinguishes the mature and cultured person from the primitive and moron.

There are indications, though, that the extent of such growth is hereditarily determined, that the individual is born to but a measured portion of freedom, that no political document is able to confer more freedom on us than we are born with, and that even education is powerless to change the stint which birth has put on us. These facts, suggested by the clinical studies of Arnold Gesell, are corroborated by reports of missionaries and anthropologists. Not infrequently the children of primitives are able to compete with the children of civilization in scholarly accomplishments. But upon entering puberty, their intellectual acumen seems wiped out; they relapse from individual achievements into species achievements, which are confined to the domains of sex, security and food. Because they seem hereditarily incapable, or less capable, of carrying the spirit of free play into adulthood, they remain arrested. Conversely, where the curiosity of youth survives the crisis of puberty, even adult life can in varying degrees escape the patterns fixed by inborn routine. In the absence of continuous instinctual tension the grooves and tunnels of animal life can expand into a truly human world of creative freedom.

Human freedom, then, is in the first place the zest of a relaxed social atmosphere and the joy of movement which is not in the biological sense utilitarian, of activity which is not the chase of the opposite sex, not the flight from, nor the pursuit of, an enemy, of deeds which are not prescribed by the hungry stomach. Free play is the bustle of liberation from the confines of the instinct tunnels and the bursting out upon the uncharted spaces of an open universe.

For good reasons, wherever the concept of freedom exists, it has become the epitome of life. It is the very essence of man's consciousness that life at its most vital and highest level is not mere existence, but evolution. Thus, after the rise of life from inert structures, a social order embodying freedom and the striving for still greater freedom represents beyond doubt the first truly new evolutionary achievement. Surely, it was the relaxed security offered by the early human family or group which freed energies that gradually led to an enrichment beyond measure of social life and to growth far beyond the animal family. And wherever such growth took place, social patterns, freed from the dissipative animal short circuits, developed commensurately with the growing mind, which was itself stimulated by the security of the social milieu, its warmth and affection.

Only now could the mobile evolutionary frontier of youth be continually extended and benefit from the adult's maturer mind. Only in a world kept at ease by social safeguards could what once were pointers to instinctual aims, "releasers" unleashing crude passions, assume values independent of the instincts. Not before all the animal instincts had found their social embodiments was man free enough to become really open-minded, world-aware, a creature with an eye for countless things, the relations between things, and the character of objects which did not serve the instincts. Only thus could human *knowledge* become possible.

It was the relaxed atmosphere of relatively secure social conditions which probably led to the discovery that a stone had more uses than to beat off an enemy and embodied values of its own— beauty, for instance. It could be playfully handled, toyed with. It was no doubt in such a playful moment that it dawned upon primitive man that a stone could be given a new shape and greater usefulness as a hammer, chisel, or saw. A branch, bending and snapping back, could now be playfully fashioned into a bow. The pelts and feathers of game hunted for food now revealed orna- mental values, and inedible plants were found to yield fibres which could be twisted into strings and yarns and woven into decorative fabrics. Not one of these developments was likely to have taken place had instinctive mechanisms alone ruled the individual's re- lations to the outside world. They became possible only where stable social conditions left the mind scope for play, freedom to let fancy roam, and to take notice of objects that have no appeal to raw instinct. The greatest driving force in human evolution, then, was not a utilitarian proclivity, but imaginative fancy mani- fest in play.[1]

The life of the wild animal is by and large one of unsteady oscillation between blinding short circuits and complete unconcern for the world about it; between fearful tension, during which in- telligence is reduced to the vanishing point, and somnolence, during which brain is of no use at all. It is a predicament similar to that of cold-blooded animals with their very rudimentary con- trol of body temperature. But just as the warm-blooded creatures disposed of a systemic dilemma by internal stabilizers, so also man has overcome the general animal dilemma by social stabilizers, social institutions. Both have in their own way realized the vital truth which the French physiologist Claude Bernard expressed in the words "The constancy of the internal milieu is the condition of a free life."

The profound importance of playfulness for human evolution is well expressed by the words we employ to characterize the arts. Music is always played and so are dramatic works. And if paintings and sculptures usually come before us as "frozen," static end products, painter and sculptor themselves are just as conscious of playing with lines, colors and clay as are musicians of playing on instruments. The novelist, too, is always toying with an idea before he furrows his brow and settles down to work. And not a few great men of science have testified that scientific creativity is no different from artistic creation. The medium is another, the basic process is the same. The scientist, too, plays with an idea, which he then tries to couch in as universal a formula as its importance permits.

More than a century and a half ago, the poet Schiller summed it up thus: "Man plays only where he is human in the fullest meaning of the word, and he is completely human only where he plays."[2] Schiller had of course learned this from the Greeks. Not by accident did the concept of freedom as a political ideal first appear among the ancient Greeks, the first people in history to know the meaning of play and who made play a national institution. To quote Edith Hamilton:[3]

> The Greeks were the first people in the world to play and they played on a grand scale. All over Greece there were games, all sorts of games . . . games so many one grows weary with the list of them. . . . If we had no other knowledge of what the Greeks were like, if nothing were left of Greek art and literature, the fact that they were in love with play and played magnificently would be proof enough of how they lived and how they looked at life. . . . Play died when Greece died and many centuries passed before it was resurrected.

But Greece herself died because, instead of for a laurel wreath, she began to play for the stake of empire; when animal instinct, in the form of commercial greed and the lust of power, made her forget fair play within her family of city-states. Of such causes all civilizations have died. They forgot, or they suppressed, free play, which fosters mind. They were victimized by their own animal instincts.

8

SELF-PRESERVATION

THE origin and nature of life is, as we saw, identical with the extension of the primary organizational principle over the relations of an open physical system and the environment. Hence every major evolutionary advance, like the appearance of multicellular creatures and of social systems, can never be anything else but the further extension of the same principle into new and higher spheres. This always means species integration, by which either any number of cells become united in a single organism, or any number of individually mobile organisms form a social system in the customary sense. In the first case, the species becomes, at least internally, the dominant part of the environment; in the latter case, also externally.

Since elemental environmental relations are always instinctual concerns, even human social evolution under the aegis of the mind is but a new way of dealing with problems as old as life itself. Now, the instinct complex is always an entity. Its aspects can therefore never be cleanly separated. Love and hatred have often been identified. The desire to consume one's partner in the act of love is familiar. And cannibalism, or even the devouring of game, combines nutrition with defense. In all these cases two instincts are involved and a third may be present overtly or covertly. In Chapter 4 we already drew attention to the complementarity of self-preservation and species preservation. This reduces the in-

stinct complex to the dimorphic form, which makes it easiest to
see that no aspect can persist without the other. If all individuals
should perish, then so would the species, and vice versa.

These conditions being rooted in the most fundamental basis of
all existence, it is obvious that they are bound to be manifest also
where the instincts have been partly sublimated through social
integration. Even in its etherealized or spiritualized state the instinct complex remains an entity. This makes the preservation of
the unity of the instinct complex a prime necessity of social evolution. For wherever functions become tangential, purposes in
themselves, they are bound to lead to dissolution, social suicide.

Now, since the animal instinct complex still forms the foundation of all vital social domains, it must be obvious that the self-
conscious mind merely devises the *forms* in which instinctually
motivated social functions can or may be realized, and these forms,
like all things social, are conventional. Since conventions merely
normalize manifestations of instinctual undercurrents, it is undoubtedly the degree of success or failure of consciously contrived
social conventions which determines whether a society or civilization evolves, stagnates or declines.

All this, in conjunction with the necessity of preserving the
entity of the instinct complex, contributes to the makeup of the
most central social problems (which sociology never saw or
avoided).

There is, first, the general and perennial question of whether
man's instincts are monitored by his mind, or whether mind becomes pander to the instincts. In the second place, there arise
questions relating to the individual instincts: to what degree may
any one of them become dominant or absolute without rupturing
the entity of the instinct complex; or, seen from the positive side,
what is the relative creative-evolutionary significance of each of
the three main instincts, i.e., its importance in sociogenesis and
evolution?

In this chapter we shall deal with the two aspects of self-preservation and in the following chapter devote ourselves to the instinct of species preservation.

LIMITATIONS OF ECONOMY

It is not difficult to show that the roots of all economic life are to be found in the food instinct and animal metabolism. Wicksteed in his book *The Common Sense of Political Economy*[1] has devoted several chapters to this demonstration.

When that disturbing situation which we call hunger arises in the individual's internal economy, he goes to market. The amount of food he buys is in the long run always determined by his physiological needs, and their intensity will even influence the price he is willing to pay. If food and drink are a matter of life and death, man will make tremendous sacrifices to obtain them, but if all his needs are taken care of, he may even refuse food and drink which are offered as gifts. The greatest skeptic must be blind not to see that here physiological conditions determine economic events, that the alimentary instinct remains a powerful social factor.

The primary purpose of social economy is, of course, none other than to enable the individual to maintain his physiological equilibrium, even though he live confined to the barren brick and concrete piles and the asphalt deserts of crowded cities, or in the country he be devoted to activities other than agriculture and the produce market.

Gradually, man has extended his economic systems over domains with no direct bearing on food, including in them all his material cares and some spiritual ones as well, such as the love of books or music or flowers. But the food needs are fundamental.

Now, there is a clearly recognizable basic relationship between the price level, as expressed in the economic law of supply and demand, and the intensity with which the animal pursues its alimentary needs. Still, it is equally obvious that the two situations belong to entirely different worlds. We have but to point out the gulf between price level (a highly sophisticated concept) and animal instinct (which may be barely conscious) to make this clear. Furthermore, the fact that prices can be manipulated attests to a certain freedom—for good or bad—in the economic sphere, and where the good-or-bad question arises, ethics comes into play. While there is no such thing as conscious ethics in the organic world, in the world of man it has become the crucial problem.

The economic domain, too, is always made up of complementary pairs similar to that comprising the animal and the object of its physiological longing. Such pairs are producer and consumer, employer and employee, supply and demand, etc. In every instance, two poles are necessary to make up a subsidiary economic field, otherwise no event can take place. You cannot sell unless you have a buyer, and you cannot buy unless you know who sells. The relationship between constituents of such pairs is always that of the fundamental complementarity of all natural events; hence any attempt on the part of one side to become absolute is bound to lead to an economic short circuit, the annihilation of the respective field. Since no economic system can endure on absolutist terms, to this extent at least social economy is fully subject to natural law.

But instinct, which persists in the individual member of the economic field, is absolute, and the "short circuit" is its apogee. From this it follows that, in a system whose nature is founded on the balance of elaborate interdependencies, the resurgence of unchecked animal appetite is always damaging. Greed, the craving for power, the will to distort the economic equilibrium to one's personal advantage, cannot but be at length destructive, subversive. It is always unethical. Every selfish interference produces a shift from creative ease to critical tension and means a reversal from ethical conduct to sheer animality with its catch-to-kill principle.

This brings us to a branch of economic life which is not merely an enlarged field of food production. With the assimilation of the male into the social fabric, the predatory instincts of hunters were also incorporated. Indeed, as almost any reputable economic history will show, large-scale commerce had its origin not so much in the exchange of agricultural produce as in robbery, piracy, plundering expeditions and raids on the herds and flocks of neighboring peoples. One of the Sanskrit (old Indo-Iranian) words for war literally means "a craving for cows." To this day a good deal of commerce bears the stamp of its predatory origins. The basic rule of the highwayman, the pirate and the robber baron was: study the map. Select as strong a topographical spot as you can find, a strategic spot through which a maximum of the region's traffic must flow. Make yourself master of that spot and take as your toll all that the traffic will bear. A medieval German *New Evangel for City Men* put it this way: "Take what is not thine and reap where thou didst not sow." In the seventeenth century the great Colbert, financier of Louis XIV of France, was still of the opinion that the only way to obtain money was to take it from others. Commerce was a war for money as military operations were for the conquest of land.

In other ways, too, capitalism, as a form of economic absolutism, betrays its descent from predatory enterprise. The concept of *venture* and unstable social conditions are central to both, and anarchy was for a long time their El Dorado. With unimpeachable logic, therefore, David Ricardo (1772–1823), one of the founders of classical economic theory, made economic insecurity an integral part of capitalistic progress. Government could only obstruct it. To this day the view survives in the minds of the stalwarts of "free enterprise," insofar as this is nothing but a euphemism for social irresponsibility and unrestrained instinctual indulgence. Congestion and competition may in many branches of commerce have necessitated certain courtesy rules according to which "the game" is to be played, but where competition can be eliminated, robbery is still the order of the day.

The perils of one-sided self-preservation are of course not confined to extremes. There is inherent in all economic activity the danger of persistent relapses into the primordial relationship between the animal and its prey. No matter how high be the material level to which man's inventions may rise in the relatively protected social environment, no matter how ingenious be the implements and gadgets with which the mind may crowd the widening sphere of free play, selfishness is bound to remain the prevalent motive in this enlarged domain of self-preservation. But by its very nature *self*-preservation is unfit for *social* dominance. It cannot but set stifling limits to man's horizon. Animal appetite, manifest in the tight holding on to things even if they cannot be eaten, acquisitiveness and possessiveness again narrow down man's freedom to something resembling the dark instinct tunnel. Thus walled up again within the widened version of the narrow self, the ego still tensely faces the outer world and remains not far removed from the blinding tautness characterizing the beast stalking its prey.

Under such conditions men, too, "lose their heads" and are no longer "their own free selves." The result generally means the missing of evolutionary opportunities because of lack of mental vision. I will give two examples here.

Old World cities and villages, built when men were still guided in most of their actions by a community spirit, and such monstrosities as are ninety-five percent of American towns and cities, all of them entrepreneurial "developments" for private profit, form a striking contrast. The first often possess an enchanting beauty, are livable because built to live in; the second are often little better than pens for human milch cows. The first are organically related to the landscape, using rivers, lakes and mountains as valuable esthetic assets enhancing human values; in the second, fruits of the profit system, beauty, because unproductive, accessible to all and free of cost, has been systematically vandalized.

Our second illustration may come as a surprise to many but will show even better to what lengths profiteering will go without the slightest return to the community of men. Until Willard Gibbs of Yale University (1839–1907) published his great work on thermodynamics, America had contributed literally nothing of consequence to science. Science was considered an unremunerative, genteel exploration of nature's curiosities. In fact, not even the epoch-making applications of science originated in the New World because none of those preoccupied with the accumulation of fortunes had vision enough to perceive their possibilities. The steam engine, the mechanical loom, the bicycle, the use of electricity for purposes of illumination (yes, even Edison had his European precursors) and in the telegraph and the telephone, the motorcar, wireless telegraphy and broadcasting, the airplane, all had their first beginnings in Europe. So had atomic physics and the groundwork for atomic energy. No country needed most of these ideas more than our vast continent, but they were not forthcoming here because of the blinding spell of money.

In sum, then, the purely economic outlook in its narrow absolutism, unaided by shots in the arm from more broadminded domains, would have left us a horde of barbarians. By itself alone, and despite the present wealth of trappings, economics is and will remain a mentally barren world. It was precisely for this reason that the great Greek philosophers, Plato and Aristotle, always spoke with scorn of those whose interests were centered on the material objects of this world. They insisted that such men—agrarians, merchants and mechanics—should be excluded from participation in politics. Nor was their argument culled from the sky. They were in a position to survey with their own eyes the catastrophic consequences of the commercial dominance of life; they were witnesses of the great suicide of the Greek city-states in armed commercial competition and their mutual betrayal to foreign powers.

Beyond any doubt, the limitations of economics belong to the prime causes of the collapse of former civilizations, usually after but a brief moment of exultation on one of the peaks of life. For most of the great civilizations the world has known were commercial civilizations which succumbed to their own predatory vices. They all destroyed themselves, destroyed their freedom and their future, like a beast of prey sinking its teeth into its own offspring, like children destroying the cardhouse they built.

The reference to animals is not a mere simile. It is a well-known

fact that instinctive mechanisms can and do break down, especially in unforeseen circumstances. Thus, in the case of the herring
gull the complex of instincts defining parental care has reference
only to the nest. If a young bird gets out of, or is removed from,
the nest, it is at once stripped of all the characters which "program" parental care and becomes an object of prey like any other
small moving creature in the environs.

Similar removals from the narrow circumstances to which primitive instincts are keyed—class barriers, economic stratification, religious differences, etc.—are responsible for countless minor and
major tragedies of civilization. Distance, geographic as well as
spiritual and intellectual, has always tended to dehumanize "the
other fellow," to deprive him of part or all of his human rights.
This still holds for the economic world, where the abstractness of
organization facilitates disposing of a victim at however great a
distance.

All this is bound to lead to mutual annihilation or self-annihilation unless new concepts of life succeed in trickling down into the
barren wilderness of a purely economic world. Economics and the
economic outlook, however necessary and vital, cannot by themselves alone save us from the fate which overtook all other economic civilizations. For, be it repeated, they are aspects of the
instinct of self-preservation, and dominant selfishness is the death
of every social world.

Where an individual instinct threatens to become absolute—
in our case that of alimentation in its social mutation, business—
the entity of the instinct complex is fractured or destroyed. Then,
according to basic law, complementarity, and with it the *conditio
sine qua non* of all existence, is annulled.

This danger has been obtrusive to only a few, but it is especially
threatening, not alone because business in general has become
near-absolute but particularly because it is on the point of dis-
solving the complementarity of the individual and the social whole.
We have developed business into an elaborate mythical rite or
materialistic theology based on increasing production for private

consumption and private profit, while almost completely neglecting communal needs and social virtues. We concentrate on the overproduction of luxurious trash, on the glutting of the market with excremental offal and its saturation with the moral stench of advertising. On the other hand, civic institutions, as supposedly unproductive, are kept at a starvation level and even, where possible, pressed into service to worsen the conditions of anarchic private enterprise. This, for example, is the case with our schools, still largely organized to train the young for the economic free-for-all, not to become public-spirited citizens.

In evolution, organic or social, the individual is never the decisive part of a complementary pair. The very concept of evolution is not applicable to the individual, but only to the species or population. We shall come back to this point in connection with the discussion of democracy (Chapter 14, on law). Here I will anticipate one point: that even economic democracy (not to be confused with literal communism or egalitarianism) is a matter of the organic complementarity of individual and society, and that the latter is the more important. This should dawn on even the pachycephalic if it is pointed out that a society can exist without rich men, but no rich man can function without a society to exploit.

The esoterics of our economic theology are based on the myth that the nation would collapse without the incentive of profit. By contrast it is reassuring to reflect that the greatest good that has ever come out of humanity appeared without such ulterior motives. All the great literature, the works of the giants in art and music, the great religions have virtually been free gifts. None of the monumental scientific milestones (out of which private fortunes are still being mined) owed its appearance to an itch for money. Perhaps more of this spirit would resurge among us if we succeeded in resuscitating the public sector of our life by freeing it from the rubble and filth of our orgiastic self-indulgence.

The trouble is that ethics is a crucial factor in the whole involved complex and that especially in politics ethics is at a discount. The essence of human evolution, though, as was shown in Chapter 6, lies in the sublimation of animal behavior into conscious conduct, the partial transmutation at least of instinct into virtues and values. Thus, in the earliest social beginnings we find writ large the paramount truth that social evolution is bound up with, and in proportion to, man's ethical development.

Nor is it social history alone which forces on us these conclusions. There are anatomical correlates which point in the same direction. In the animal organism economic problems are taken care of by automatic physiological chain reactions governed from some instinctive midbrain center. In man, on the other hand, these midbrain centers have become very much reduced, and the thinking cerebral cortex has taken over many of the functions which in the lower mammals are automatic and have their seats in the lower brain. Man must therefore rely on conscious thought as much as the animal can rely on its instincts for the regulation of environmental relations.

The least, however, that we can ask of conscious relations is that they be governed by reason. And since the individual's reasoning powers are unquestionably the fruit of social processes, his relations, too, must be ruled not by his narrow, selfish, one-dimensional logic but by the higher, multidimensional, the more universal "social logic," which is ethics.

The ethical solution of social, particularly economic, problems therefore is a concomitant of, and a mandate implied in, human cerebral anatomy. Social man—and that includes all strata—without an ethic more reliable than the instincts he has sacrificed to consciousness, in the end must perish as surely as the animal without instincts would perish.

And finally, let us remind ourselves again of the "great bifurcation" in earliest evolution, the splitting off from the main, organic, course of an inert, mechanical branch. The institutions of civilized economic life, too, are overwhelmingly mechanical affairs. But the fundamental order of the world, at least that aspect of it which made evolution possible, is nonmechanical. As far as life and evolution are concerned, mechanism, or its dominance, is always a form of degeneracy, a way into a dead end.

LIMITATIONS OF DEFENSE

The natural history of man's warlike nature is a chapter of evolution concerning which learned opinion is far from having crystallized. In fact there is presently dominant, especially in Anglo-American academes, a romantic Sunday-school theology which peremptorily denies man any innate aggressiveness and maintains that where it erupts to spite the beauty of the faith it is merely the result of frustration. Such situations frequently arise where theories are founded on odds and ends and lead a sort of "departmental remittance existence" with not the slightest ties to the actualities of life. From the point of view maintained in this discourse, the matter assumes a different face. That living creatures know amity as well as enmity is intrinsic in the organism-environment complementarity. This determines an inward as well as an outward orientation on all evolutionary levels: inner cohesion, cooperation or at least tolerance, and toward the environment wariness, defensiveness and even aggression. Nothing confirms this better than the above-mentioned coteries themselves, who can become arrogantly aggressive—for example, when reviewing a book by a member of an out-group, say, Konrad Lorenz.

Why has the killing of one's kind assumed such extravagant proportions in the human sphere, whereas it is virtually unknown among our nearest animal relations? Within the new science, to which the very concept of matter has become questionable, answers proffered from the traditional premise of anatomic-physiological materialism are evidently not very helpful. We must begin with the recognition that man is, above all, a mental creature. No mind, no man. This makes it virtually *de rigeur* to promote to prominence a certain evolutionary discontinuity best expressed in this way: in the human sphere, speciation (the central problem of evolution) becomes *mental speciation.*

I shall deal with this matter in greater detail in Chapter 10 and here must confine myself to anticipating some of the main points. Primitive cultures as well as civilizations, that is, the peculiar mentalities which gave rise to them, in all likelihood have a genetic basis. If we at all concede the existence of mind, the inference becomes justified that cultures and civilizations are manifestations of mental speciation, or at least incipient mental speciation. What sets men apart is not so much anatomical, but mental or cultural divergences: differences of language, even of dialect, of religion, custom, etc. These are, as was pointed out in Chapter 5, all-important to the extent that a primitive tribe may consider itself the only true human species, the chosen people, the master race. Other tribes and peoples thus become as "legitimate" objects of aggression as one animal species may be to another. In other words, what is abnormal, intraspecific aggression from the zoological point of view becomes, if we accept mental speciation as an evolutionary fact, normal interspecific aggression. The concept of mental speciation cuts through a minor Gordian knot of evolutionary theory. It accounts for the fact that on primitive (and not so primitive) levels those not belonging to the tribe, the village, nation or faith, those speaking another language and wearing different dress become excluded from what constitutes the local concept of man, are dehumanized, removed to a spiritual distance where, as in the case of the herring gull devouring its own young, the normal inhibitions break down.

It is not to be doubted that during prehistoric, and even early historic phases of human development warfare was a most powerful selective agent, weeding out the less fit and allowing only the fittest to propagate their kind. We cannot wholly deplore it, for we ourselves are the fruits of such selection, and it is not an altogether pleasant occupation to reflect on what we would be like today without it. However, like other evolutionary trends, the penchant for aggression was bound to reach a point of diminishing returns, beyond which excesses ultimately became self-defeating.

This is obvious throughout most of recorded history and never more so than today. If, as was indicated, purely economic orientation is unfit for social dominance, this is even truer of the dynamic component of the instinct of self-preservation. Economic life, in spite of its shortsightedness, is basically still a constructive, or at least a conservative factor, but defense and aggression have always been negative affairs. So that, while economic dominance of life is crippling, military dominance is generally killing, particularly where the apparatus of defense becomes an instrument of aggression for aggression's sake. Toynbee, in A *Study of History*,[2] has assembled an impressive array of evidence.

The great Assyrian–Babylonian empire, after an existence of two thousand years, succumbed to its military arrogance; it became depopulated, economically starved, choked, as it were, by its own armor. Sparta, by turning the state into a highly specialized war machine, from the outset ruined her chances to become a truly civilized member of the Greek community of city-states and is perhaps the purest example of a robber nation. The Roman and the East Roman empires, the empire of Timur Leng and, in our own age, Mussolini's Italy, Hitler's Third Reich, and Tojo's Japan have furnished outstanding examples of the perversion of military defense into instruments of aggression and the consequent self-defeat of the aggressors. To this day, France has hardly recovered from the militarism of the Revolutionists and the two Napoleonic debacles. For over a century and a half she has given the spectacle of a chain reaction of crises, of political immaturity, of a nation kept from expiring only by the grace of other nations.

Even more than economic institutions, military ones are pure machines and hence, if allowed to become an end in themselves, are bound to bring about a new evolutionary bifurcation leading to a new dead end. Furthermore—contrary to the economic field, which for a long time remained primarily one of individual activity —the domain of defense from the beginning comprised the main body of the male population and therefore is usually the first to become socialized, the first in which the state becomes absolute.

The dominance of the defensive apparatus thus inevitably leads to totalitarianism: all armed services are totalitarian by nature. The more efficient they are in their narrow negative way, the more easily they become a temptation and a model to be imitated by civil and other institutions which have, or ought to have, positive aims. Thus the negativism of defense affects conservative and constructive functions, always, of course, at the cost of a heavy retrenchment of freedom and creative initiative. To give but two examples: the progressive militarization of the civil service in eighteenth- and nineteenth-century Prussia led to an almost complete cultural stagnation; and in the Middle Ages the corruption of the Roman Church held pace with the tightening of her organization as a militant fascist theocracy. Stagnation and degeneration always accompany the rise of militarism. The complementarity of individual and state (of which we shall speak in Chapters 13 and 14) becomes upset, and with the displacement of the fundamental condition of freedom by an absolute statism, the body politic is slowly reduced to the status of a lifeless machine.

Yet, as previously indicated, we can neither condemn nor condone these developments altogether. During the earliest period of human history, the defensive instinct achieved at least a partial sublimation. It is not by accident that we use terms like "attack," "campaign," "war," "conquest," "victory" in speaking of our dealings with objects not in the least resembling a living enemy. Today we employ these terms regularly with reference to our scientific, technical, artistic and moral problems. In short, a good part of man's inquisitive and enterprising mentality, his love of spiritual conquests, his urge to subdue nature, must likewise be regarded as sublimated aggressiveness.

The drawback was that this gain in mental powers only sharpened the cruder struggles between human groups. So that in the course of thousands of years an intense selection pressure favoring belligerency produced human breeds in which aggressiveness assumed a virtually religious aura. This is plainly apparent already in early Biblical history, as well as in the wars of Islam and in modern chauvinism. The most recent refinements in the techniques of warfare, together with the overpopulation of the world (also partly due to man's scientific conquests), have finally brought us to an impasse *sans pareil*. Further developments in the same direction can only mean our complete undoing. A basically vital instinct has reached an extreme where it is liable to become treason against the species.

To sum up: defense, like business, is in no respect fit for social dominance because, by definition, any aspect of *self*-preservation falls short of the comprehensive entity of a *social* world. If as a wholly negative function, defense is carried to extremes and becomes aggression for aggression's sake, it is bound to degenerate into complete self-annihilation. It, too, ruptures the vital unity of the instinct complex on which evolution depends. It knows no love but thrives on hatred, and even in its less objectionable forms represents a severe drain on the positive assets of a people. (How magnificently we could enrich our physical and spiritual environment if there were no military budget!)

In general, all manifestations of self-preservation, even in their less excessive utterances, by their very nature mean self-*limitation*. This is apparent throughout the scale of life. The child who declines, or is unable, to accept anything from others remains ineducable, an idiot. The adult who refuses to associate with others cannot make a living. And at the bottom of the evolutionary ladder we have those protista which reproduce asexually and which are sometimes held up to us as the only "immortal" creatures. Actually, they never die (except if eaten). They merely divide in two, the two into four, etc., so that all individuals existing today may, in a sense, be said to reach back directly, to have "lived," two billion years. Here is self-preservation in as pure a form as nature allows. That it is also self-limitation is evident from the fact that these creatures have remained protista (one-celled beings), untouched by evolution these two billion years.

By and large, evolution, especially higher evolution, was made possible only through sexual reproduction, which from the beginning involved self-sacrifice, the giving up of their identity by two individual cells, their merger and subsequent redivision into two individuals differing from both parents. But this self-sacrifice goes further. It leads to death. All sexually reproducing forms of life must die. The individual sacrifices its *self* in order to open up all the avenues of evolution to the *species*.

With some justification, therefore, we may look upon the instincts of self-preservation as vestiges of protistan life and at best as safe guides only to eternal stagnation.

9

SPECIES PRESERVATION

A s everybody is aware, the subject of species preservation is to
some extent identical with that of sex; but whereas the
verbiage devoted to purely animalic sex would fill library
upon library, the evolutionary, sociophilosophical significance of
species preservation has been given scant attention, even by sociologists and political philosophers.

Yet the fact alone that the reproductive instinct is *the primary
social instinct* should make it obvious that its evolutionary role
surpasses the purely sexual aspect. A primary factor is a fundamental factor and likely to remain basic in all its evolutionary
transfigurations.

Biologically, sexual reproduction rests on the halving of the
number of chromosomes in both parent cells and after the merger
of these the shuffling together of the elements of heredity into a
combination which is unique. Both these processes involve more
chance than system. And though the geneticists like to speak of the
mechanics of reproduction, not even the most daring physicists
would try to reduce it to a rigid formula. The "mechanics" here
is largely wishful thinking or inappropriate analogy. On this freedom from strict mechanism is based the possibility of evolution as
well as, one is inclined to think, the fact that the danger of mechanization (and hence of evolutionary dead ends) is ever remote

in those ultimate efflorescences of species preservation of which we shall treat in this chapter.

It was pointed out that sexual reproduction, even on the lowest levels of life, to a degree at least discards self-preservation and calls for self-sacrifice, something that transcends the individual. Moreover, down the millions of years of life on our planet, the essence of evolution—on the multicellular as on the multi-individual level —has been *species integration*, and integration too, on whatever level, is possible only on the basis of something transcending the constituent units. In fact, species *integration* is but an aspect of species *preservation*.

A further point of importance is this: whereas in the domains of economy and defense (self-preservation) vegetative and dynamic factors operate disjointedly, species preservation and its social institutionalization in marriage and the family, unite in a complementary relationship both vegetative-static and dynamic-animalic elements (in the sense of our basic definitions). We have sufficiently stressed the importance of complementarity in all creative-evolutionary processes. By comparison, food instinct and defense instinct, and their social upshots, are, so to speak, merely old-maid and bachelor concerns and without issue. The future has always belonged to the pairing instinct.

All these fundamental aspects of reproduction justify the hope that we may find in the reproductive domain potentials capable of overcoming the stalemates presented by the two instincts of self-preservation, i.e., the fields of economy and defense. The primary social instinct, even on the lowest animal levels, evinces concerns eminently vaster than those of the two strictly private instincts. It is, in the fullest meaning of the term, the transcendental instinct, the guardian, as it were, of the species.

SUBLIMATION OF THE REPRODUCTIVE INSTINCT

As nutrition in the social atmosphere brought forth ethical phenomena like diligence, industry and economy, and defense blossomed into courage, loyalty, trust, responsibility and spiritual conquest, so also the reproductive instinct has its ethical sublimate. It is known as *love*.[1]

Characteristically for our materialistic age, we feel embarrassed if confronted with this word. Outside of poetry and homilies it is a favorite target of the cynics, while among more objective minds opinions are as varied as on any theological topic. There are biologists as well as theologians who categorically deny that love has anything to do with sex, but at least one biologist would not even deny the ethico-emotional experience of love to the mice in his cellar, and another to ducks and geese.

For the purposes of this study we may well assume as a certainty that, as far as man is concerned, love in its highest and most intense forms is above all a spiritual experience and a distillate of more elemental biological powers. An evolutionary inquiry going beyond Homo sapiens as a hominid, i.e., beyond mere anatomy, can therefore hardly evade the task of looking at love as an evolutionary factor of first magnitude. It can under no circumstances be ignored out of existence. A spiritual experience, however, is a form of mental experience. And since nobody has as yet been able to put his finger on the exact evolutionary point where mind first becomes demonstrable, the possibility cannot be excluded that in some way and to some degree mind—and hence love—is identical with life.

Since life, however, has not arisen out of nothing, the beginnings of mind and of love may still lie in a deeper stratum. When, in a former context, we metaphorically called complementarity "the marriage of harmonious opposites," we did, in a way, identify love with the prime cause of all. And certainly in the more perspicuous world of the human mind love's close relationship with complementarity should not be hard to recognize. For is it not the deep innate certainty, conscious or unconscious, which perhaps no creature lacks, that life is interdependence, the going hand-in-hand, the carrying of and being carried by others? With man, in any case, it is the reveling in, and the veneration of, what we depend on, what means fulfillment.

In some of his dialogues Plato speaks of it as *eros*, makes it the property of the female and assigns it to the lowliest levels of life. On the other hand, he speaks of the highest form of the mind, and the exclusive prerogative of the male, as *logos*. The distinction has its uses, though we need not accept it hide and hair with the moral and intellectual scale of values the Greek philosopher attached to it.

The fact is, though, that on primitive animal levels the male usually shows a higher sensory-nervous development than the female. Yet evolutionarily both the earliest organs of reproduction and of the mind can be traced back to a common origin, the ectoderm (the outer of two layers) of the two-tissue animals. This was the first organ specializing in environmental relations, and thought and reproduction have, biologically speaking, remained the dominant "transcendental" functions, the main links with those parts of the world without which no creature can live—the environment as a whole and the species as the most important part of the environment, from which comes all fulfillment and which embodies the future. Thus love (*eros*) and thought (*logos*) have remained aspects of one thing, a complementary pair. Here again we find ourselves face to face with the continuity of the most basic principle.

Even in the sense in which Niels Bohr applied the term complementarity to phenomena of life, it always meant the integration of two opposites in a new entity of a superior order, of such a nature that no component has any real meaning by itself alone. In exactly this sense, thought and love have remained aspects of one thing. In other words, even the mind remains sex-linked, as is most evident in the lower animal kingdom. The greater aptitude of the primitive male animal for "learning" and "knowledge," based in its more highly developed sensory-nervous system, is strictly confined to learning the female's whereabouts and to the "knowledge" of the female. The *logos* finds its fulfillment in the complementary *eros*, and out of the resultant short circuit, in which the male is often sacrificed, new life will rise again.

Since the principle of complementarity is universal, we are bound to find it manifest also in the world of man. In the reproductive field the human male, too, always finds himself face to face with the other side of the species holding out the promise of fulfillment. And in order to find fulfillment he must serve the species. There is always in this event a sort of reenactment on a higher level of the expiration of the individual for the sake of the species, which began with the first appearance of sexual reproduction. The ego must die, and craves to die, if only for a moment, so that the species may live.

Much more than we are usually willing to admit, the event is a function of the species rather than of the individual. It is a complementary function ordained, as it were, by the species. And herein lies its great evolutionary significance, for evolution is above all a species event. And this, finally, brings us to the main point of this chapter. While defense and nutrition, as instinctive phenomena, basically concern only the self, reproduction has reference to the species, and precisely for this reason it is within its powers to open up a breach in the formidable barrier with which the self-centered instincts are liable to hem man in. The selfish instincts alone would never have led to any notable degree of species integration; their end is the short circuit. The reproductive instinct, on the other hand, is creative. Because it derives its incentives from that "transcendental" entity, the species, there are on both sides factors transcending the ego, and it is these factors alone which can guide evolution to the attainment of superindividual entities. The earliest of these is the institution of marriage. Here, and nowhere else, begins the integration of the species in the spirit of the new evolution, in which coherence is essentially mental, where functions are accordingly freer, and where, as a matter of principle, there is no limit to their radiations.

We are here dealing with an evolutionary process which, generally speaking, has perhaps not yet gone beyond its initial phases and whose course remains beset with difficulties. In the connubial tie the transcendental instinct always finds itself allied with the self-centered ones, which, being more ingrained than ethereal love, easily gain the upper hand. The result often is that *eros* is degraded to a mere object in the male field of prey, to chattel, and the most creative of the primal instincts becomes a victim of barren economic man. The male is again absolute, chasing down narrow instinct tunnels, or pursuing *logos* in such opprobrious counterfeits as the "enlightened self-interest" of classical liberalism. The hopeful breach in the vicious circle of the instincts is closed again, and what evolution still takes place must confine itself to secondary or lesser aspects of the social world, its purely material side.

Still, we need not remain blind to the fact that historically even such retardation had its positive side. Material possessions and material progress did aggrandize the ego and help pry the individual out of the diffuse amorphousness of the primitive ethnic group. Only a sufficiently enhanced ego could, in bending back from its extreme pursuit of extraneous aims and knowledge, be sensitized enough to realize that what he was experiencing in the "primary social event" was not pure animalic sex, but something more: fulfillment in its widest spiritual sense through a complementary ego. Only in such love could the egocentric individual learn permanently to transcend himself.

All this should be regarded not as a neoromantic or neomystic doctrine but quite objectively as a crucial part of the new evolution. Love is in truth the supreme form of complementarity accessible to individual experience. That is why in its various metamorphoses it is of the essence of the new evolution.

What, then, are the wider social radiations of love and its transmutations?

Among evolutionists it is an accepted truth that because every living system is an integral whole, any particular or local innovation makes itself felt throughout the system, be it organic or social. The sublimations of the reproductive instinct form no exception. Gradually this humanizing of an animal instinct provided man with a new outlook on life, a new and deeper perspective which, to some degree at least, could not but transform the two self-centered instincts as well as the social domains they dominate, and thus clear barriers to species integration on an increasingly larger scale.

In the first place, it had perhaps its greatest influence on the purely rational component of the human mind. Only under the impact of a love which is more than instinctual sex could loving *contemplation* become possible, i.e., the dispassionate study of all objects and phenomena for their own innate values. Only thus transformed could man at last become truly *knowing* and objectively *devoted* to things other than the object of his love; because in the words of W. H. Sheldon,[2] "in mere contemplation attention is enlarged rather than concentrated." Or, as Schiller[3] long ago formulated it, "Whereas desire seizes its object immediately, contemplation removes it into the distance and makes it its true inalienable possession precisely by rescuing it from passion."

Neither science nor art nor philosophy, whose essence is objective, loving devotion, free of instinctual prompting, would have had a chance to arise among men without the prior sublimation of the transcendental instinct.

Thus alone could species preservation, through its etherealizations, gradually become a love potentially embracing all and everything. Only this self-transcending instinct could lift man above the animal level, to which the other instincts were liable to keep him confined. For here, above all, man painfully experienced that the more he subjected the object of his love to mere passion, the more possession became one with death. Only by relinquishing every proprietary claim in love could man find the largest possible freedom and attain the highest ethos: the esteem of the other person. Thus alone could venery be transfigured into veneration. Only in this way could man learn that the most precious goods cannot be wrenched from others but must be freely given. From this small seed alone could gradually grow the general respect of man for man, the love of one's fellowmen, and what the eighteenth century called "the rights of man."

Thus love leads into politics.

LOVE AND POLITICS

If the foregoing seemed too metaphysical for the reader, he may
disregard it; for we arrive at virtually identical results by considerations more down to earth. The wisest of the sages have always
known love as the greatest sociogenic factor. Confucius[4] said,
"The ancient rulers regarded loving the people as the chief principle of their government. . . . So love and respect are the
foundations of government." To Empedocles, love was the greatest
moving force in the universe, the final cause of all. In the original
Christian doctrine, too, love became the one great life-giving force
and man's only salvation. "We know that we have passed from
death unto life, because we love the brethren. He that loveth not
his brethren abideth in death."

But again I wish to emphasize the need of considering all this
with the greatest objectivity, as probably the most crucial complex
of social problems. The unique role of love as the keystone, so to
speak, of the grand vault of social architecture arises, we have
seen, from the fact that it is the transfigured form of the one self-
transcending and integrative instinct. Social systems based exclusively on the two instincts of self-preservation and neglecting the
selfless primary social instinct and its sublimations—the *énergie
créatrice qui serait amour* of Bergson—are literally crippled systems and generally short-lived. The primary social instinct cannot
in its spiritual form be allowed to suffer a setback to the advantage
of the nonsocial, selfish instincts. Unless all three basic instincts
are jointly and harmoniously sublimated into ethico-rational
values, the whole of the social structure must fall apart, or can be
held together only by brute authoritarian force. This is what makes
love a sociopolitical factor of prime importance.

Its greatest significance must be sought in its potentiality to
transcend not alone the self, but all personal relations, in its radiations into all human concerns, particularly the fields of the
instincts of self-preservation. If social evolution is *species integration* on the highest, mental level of life, it must be self-evident

that none of the self-centered instincts can indefinitely remain dominant, but only the instinct of *species preservation* and its ethical efflorescences. This is the spirit of love. All else is liable to become social treason, treason against the species.

Even a command like "Love your enemies" therefore arises logically and imperiously from these fundamentals of biosocial evolution. We may realize in shame that we are as yet far from its fulfillment. Still, we no longer slaughter prisoners of war nor assault every stranger coming our way as only a few centuries ago was still customary in certain regions of the pseudo-Christian West. There has, then, been progress. So there is hope that transmuted love, which blossomed forth from the province of the primary social instinct, may in time—as friendship, respect, reverence, the recognition of every individual as one's equal—embrace wider and wider circles.

Obviously, there is no room yet for such love in the tight tribal body based on blood bonds or the universal "chosen people" of primitivity. Advanced civilizations always need the spiritual hybridizing and cross-pollination possible only in the flocking together and the living together of many not related by blood, though kindred in spirit. Great civilizations can develop only where, and because, blood bonds, the vestiges of primordial physiological organization, give way to purely mental bonds. This is no doubt the essential meaning of one of Christ's profoundest and least understood sayings: "For I am come to set a man at variance against his father, and a daughter against her mother, and a daughter-in-law against her mother-in-law. A man's foes shall be they of his own household."[5]

History corroborates this, even modern psychology confirms it: man's closest kin have usually been his worst fetters. Herein lies, for instance, the epochal importance of the political reform of Cleisthenes (ca. 500 B.C.), the decisive step in the transition from a tribal to a free, functional organization, and the overture to Athens' flowering. But long before classical Athens, the evolutionary possibilities of free communal organization (free because free from the shackles of genealogical organization) were demonstrated by the Greek settlers on the coast of Asia Minor. These, as Toynbee[6] points out, perpetuated in the civic organizations of their new homelands the free organizations of ship's companies of emigrants. "On shore as at sea, comradeship would count for more than kin, and the orders of a chosen and trusted leader would override the promptings of habit and custom. In fact, a bevy of ship's companies . . . in a strange land would turn spontaneously into a city-state . . . governed by an elective magistracy." These Greek city-states of Asia Minor became the inspirers of everything that later achieved greatness in the Greek "old world," such as the freedom of democratic institutions, art, literature, science and philosophy.

The history of language offers further testimony in support of our thesis. Indeed, linguistic history proves that what may seem new to us at one time was common knowledge. The words "free" and "friend" (and the corresponding German and Scandinavian forms) are derived from a common root denoting "love." A related Anglo-Saxon word, *frithu* (German *Friede*), means a condition of general goodwill, devotion, respect, love and peace. A friend hence is one who is loved and who loves, who enjoys the protection of general peace and love. A free man was always one loved by all, and freedom never anything but the fruit of love.

True freedom therefore is remote from the negative laissez-faire of shallow traditional liberalism, which was never better than the freedom of a kind of prostitution, a social corrosive, social treason. Instead of assuring that loving-kindness and peace which was the original meaning of freedom, it led to a war of all against all. The truly free society therefore can only be one in which animal greed and the lust for power (still manifestations of instinctive animal mechanisms) recede before the respect of man for man.

None of us can pretend already to embody all that such love could be, though many of us probably realize in which direction betterment is to be sought. It is indeed even difficult not to allow a certain pessimism to prevail here. Yet attempts must continue to find a solution of the problem. Because, whether we like it or not, it is virtually the core of the problem of further evolution. All else is ephemeral fashion of no greater importance than sartorial novelties. The plain hard truth, then, which, if we are the realists we proudly call ourselves, we ought to begin to realize is that social evolution can extend no further than the ethic of binding love permits.[7] For "love" is but an old-fashioned term for the highest form of ethic.

If love is but an old-fashioned term for ethic, if ethic is complementarity risen to consciousness, and if we now look at the evolutionary problem at issue, we cannot fail to see that love is indeed the triune complementarity of the whole (sublimated) instinct complex. It cannot, like business and warfare, be a purpose in itself. It cannot become absolute and thus rupture the vital instinct complex. Instinctually it is all in one. For love not only loves, it cannot be love unless it also protects and nourishes.

Here we have come upon the central fact of every science of society. All the rest of sociology is often little more than academic gossip with no relation whatsoever to fundamental science.

Yet why have two thousand years of the gospel of love left the world much as it ever was, with but the trimmings slightly altered? Perhaps we can come closest to the core of the problem if we remember that Francis of Assisi preached the Gospel to the birds, which nevertheless have remained mere birds. The answer we are looking for thus seems to be that we may first have to breed a race of men fit for the Gospel. Certainly Priority Project Hurry of the social engineers and the politicians in their tow would seem the worst way to reach the goal. It looks, then, as if the Gospel just happened to strike a profound scientific truth, without realizing what genetic problems are involved. But whether we of this day are ready to apply genetics to the problem is another question.

Moreover, we have so far considered the ethical question only as one of personal relations, i.e., a purely social question. We are, however, living in a political world which, as we shall see in the following chapters, is a world belonging to a quite different dimension or sphere of life. How the ethical problem appears from that more advanced stage we cannot judge before we have gained a clear conception of what political life really means within the total evolutionary perspective.

Summing up: of the three main instincts the primary social instinct alone can, in its sublimated form, offer any hope for continuous evolution, for it is the instinct of species preservation, and all evolution is species evolution. As the embodiment of the world's primary principle it is also that of an "escalator" principle not tied to any limits. Being irrational and organic, love is supremely immune to mechanistic regimentation and hence can potentially remain in the mainstream of evolution. And finally, it assures the necessary balance and the unity of the instinct complex, whereas the dominance of either of the two selfish instincts, tending to become absolute, inevitably leads into blind alleys of dead mechanism. Mechanism, remember, is a secondary phenomenon in cosmic evolution, a very useful servant but a treacherous master, the hope and idol only of fools and living corpses. Life, on the other hand, has its roots in the primary stratum of existence, which is organic.

PART THREE

Political Man

The problem is not how to produce great men, but how to produce great societies.
ALFRED NORTH WHITEHEAD

And the high destiny of the individual is to serve rather than to rule, or to impose himself in any other way.
ALBERT EINSTEIN

10

THE GERM OF POLITICS

A s we now turn our attention to one of the most extraordinary features of all evolution, it is perhaps not out of place to remind the reader of what was said in the beginning: that originally "political" man meant "civilized" man. The concept of civilization has, though, undergone certain modifications. Over the centuries the emphasis has shifted away from what we call "political" to those secondary but larger manifestations now subsumed under the term "civilization." Nevertheless, evolutionarily the strictly political aspects of the phenomenon to be investigated are primary. Hence, trying to understand civilized man, or the origin of civilization, without regard to politics is like trying to understand a fish without the water that is its element.

Two facts of political life are sure indications that what it has so far achieved is of an abominably dilettantish nature. First, no civilization has ever achieved permanence. Second, as compared with the organizational refinement even of an animal of low rank, our political institutions are excessively crude. For these reasons this part of our inquiry will somewhat differ from the two preceding ones. As there is little sense in devoting a serious study to artistic dilettantism, neither is there sense in wasting much time on the details of political Rube Goldberg contraptions. We shall, therefore, more than in the first two parts, concentrate on fundamentals, historical facts and the demonstration that political evolution *is* part of natural evolution and cannot profitably be viewed apart from the general principles that guided evolution as a whole. What our civilization would seem to need more than anything else is an army of political naturalists and fewer political tinkers. We must, hence, start once more from first principles.

THE SEXES IN ANIMAL HISTORY

In the series of complementary pairs referred to in Chapter 1 it is implied that social life in the narrower sense is of a relatively static-vegetative-female nature, while political life represents the dynamic-animalic-male aspect of the most recent evolutionary phase. Because a great deal of what is to follow depends on a clear understanding of this formulation, it is necessary to trace the difference between the two complementary aspects through successive evolutionary phases.

Throughout the rising scale of evolution the modes of life of the two sexes are often different. The female represents the relatively static, the male the relatively more dynamic side of the species. In the Phylum Vertebrata this is evident, for instance, in the circumstance that the immature of both sexes, reflecting the past of the species, always resemble the female, whereas it is the adult males, with their showy feathers, combs, long spurs, their manes, beards, and often horns, that are the revolutionaries, originating new fashions in animal dress. With many fishes, salamanders and birds, the males change appearance at least during the breeding season and break out in the showiest colors. Furthermore, throughout the animal kingdom the male is the more mobile of the sexes. Indeed, one is tempted categorically to say that all higher forms of animal motility are inventions of the male sex. This refers not only to horseback riding and travel by boat, wagon and other mechanical inventions, but even to the acquisition of bodily wings. For good reason the angels of old, at least in our Western world, were always males. Even the superstitious ancients had enough intuitive knowledge not to suspect women of the invention of flight. Certainly in the insect world of today species are common in which only the males fly, whereas the females remain grounded, almost rooted like plants on or near the spot where they were hatched. Many aphids and moths belong to this group. The male, forced to search for the relatively stationary female, also requires a more highly developed apparatus of orientation, greater "intelligence" than the female, so that, as has already been said, it becomes even on lowly evolutionary levels (in a purely subrational sense, of course) the "striving," "knowledge-seeking" half of the species.

This picture, however, has its obverse. The female has qualities which compensate for her backwardness in sensory-motor development. As soon as we reach the level of evolution where multi-cellular organization expands into multi-individual, the advantages appear all on the side of the vegetative female. For reasons of size, groups and societies are usually confined to a more static existence than is the individual, and it is fully consistent with the relatively static nature of the female that in most animal species it became *the* social sex. Nor is the case unique. For if we survey terrestrial evolution as a whole, we cannot help becoming a little more modest in our estimate of the progressiveness of the dynamic-animalic-male branches of the tree of existence. Plants, for instance, were present on earth before the animals because no animal can live except on food prepared by plants. And quite definitely, within the Class Mammalia the female was the social pioneer.

There is another, and highly important, side to complementary pairs as we find them everywhere. We can briefly sum it up thus: the evolutionary possibilities innate in their protonic-static components are always less than those intrinsic in the electronic-animalic. This becomes evident, for instance, in the greater variety found in the latter category, as compared with the former. On the atomic level, for example, the number of different nuclei, i.e., the number of potential chemical elements, is restricted to about a hundred, whereas the number of possible molecules, resulting from the interweaving of the "orbits" of electrons, is virtually unlimited. Similarly, the number of animal species is about four or five times that of plant species, even though the mass of plants is immeasurably greater than that of the earth's animals. Of even greater evolutionary importance is a second difference between the constituents of complementary pairs. The development of the protonic-static sides is, so to speak, restricted to the "horizontal" dimension. It exhausts itself in conquest by diffusion, proliferation. Outstanding "vertical" evolution is the prerogative of the electronic-animalic sides. Hence, where the static aspect is dominant, developmental prospects are relatively insignificant. In the most primitive organisms, for example, the conservative nucleus dominates virtually the entire life of the cell, as it still does in plants and the vegetative tissues of animals. But in the higher protozoans and in the muscle and nerve tissues of higher animals, the cytoplasm has achieved a certain autonomy, a life of its own fairly independent of the cell nucleus. It is this shift from protonic-nuclear dominance to greater and greater electronic-cytoplasmic articulation which made possible the tremendous "vertical" range of animal evolution. It accounts, on the one hand, for the relatively small difference between a primitive plant like a fern and a flowering plant such as a chrysanthemum and, on the other hand, for the tremendous difference, for example, between an earthworm and a mammal.

All this is corroborated by social evolution. In every domain of animal life female dominance meant essentially plantlike ramping, spreading out, but very little "upward" movement, little evolutionary progress and early stagnation. The most instructive, and truly startling, examples of social arrestment are furnished by the insect societies, all of which are essentially female societies. Among bees, the males or drones are not part of the organization at all, but parasites, whereas among ants and termites they are mostly castrates. Hence, female dominance is absolute, and so has been stagnation ever since these six-legged girl scouts achieved the marvels of their organizations. According to the experts, they have been merely marking time for anything from fifty to a hundred million years.

Male dominance is not unknown in the animal kingdom but has never progressed beyond the initial stages, the mere show of strength, which entails extremely limited organizational, that is, evolutionary potentialities, just as does political pugilism. The best-known cases are those to which the name "pecking order" has been given. Such an order is like a bureaucratic-military hierarchy in which you may kick and peck your inferiors, whereas you bow and scrape before your superiors. We may call them inchoate political orders, but they are all so primitive as hardly to warrant further consideration. We must turn to the human species to understand the full import of the difference between the vegetative-female and the animalic-male order of life.

THE ORIGIN OF CIVILIZATION

To the cloistered historian and to the cultural anthropologist out of touch with the broader aspects of life, the staggering differences between human primitivity and advanced civilization has been a source of unending riddles and confusion. This accounts for the recent superficial division of the history of peoples into "preliterate" and "literate" periods. It is about as pertinent as would be the cutting up of Western history into a "breeches era" and a "pantaloons era," presuming that the characteristic traits of both were owing to the respective legwear. Haberdashery standards, whether graphic or sartorial, are of course meaningless in evolution. We know that many of the outstanding personages of the early phases of civilizations could neither read nor write, and we know as well that today countless "primitives" teach reading and writing in the schools. Literacy or illiteracy has nothing to do with the distinction between civilization and primitivity. On the other hand, these older terms are in close agreement with evolutionary facts. To anticipate the main point: primitivity was a phase of female dominance, whereas male dominance made possible civilizations.

Man, in the meaning of Homo faber, the maker of tools, has existed for perhaps half a million years or longer. But human *history*, that phase of human existence marked by dramatic events, dynamic movements, a tremendous evolution of social systems as to size and complexity, variety of undertakings and diversification of forms, has been a matter of a mere six thousand years. It is confined to *civilizations*.

What is civilization? For present purposes no other definition but one in agreement with general scientific theory will do. We shall try to lead up to it in stages.

Human, or quasi-human, creatures living in families, groups or bands obviously are a direct continuation of animal existence and represent what is commonly called the primitive stage of evolution. The general view has so far been that the transition to civilization was gradual, similar to that of the child turning into an adult. This seems to me an unacceptable analogy for the reason, chiefly, that, whereas all normal children become adults, the majority of human tribes have never attained a civilization, and masses of primitives have survived within all civilizations. One is hence constrained to assume that primitivity is one state of mind and civilization another. And this invites drawing a parallel between the emergence of civilization from primitivity and the branching off of one animal species from another.

We here return to a subject already touched upon in Chapter 8—*mental speciation*. It was said there that the differences between human groups, races, etc., are not so much anatomical as mental or cultural. In the present context that would mean that primitivity and civilization represent two mental species or, more appropriately, different mental genera, of which the younger descended from the older. Now, the origin of a new species or genus is always allied with a change in the genetic constitution, and it hence remains to show that even "mental speciation," the rise of the "civilized species" (or genus), has a genetic base. A full account would require more space than can here be given to the problem, so a brief outline must suffice. The argument can be summed up in a few points.

(1) Human primitivity, beyond doubt, was a development from

the normal mammalian family, in which the male rarely has a place. (2) For this reason it received its deepest imprints from the mothers. The males, as is still the case in the most primitive surviving societies, held positions of secondary importance. (3) In primitivity, as a mammalian-matronal order, orientation is still predominantly biological, concerned with the raising of the young, reproduction in general, and the problems of nutrition and defense. (4) However, as the first extension of mammalian life from the purely biological into the mental sphere, primitivity did mean a phenomenal "leap" from automatic-physiological regulation of interindividual relations to mental regulation. In other words, it represents the supersedure of an instinctual by an *ethical* order.

How, now, does civilization compare with this? We can again reduce the argument to four main points. (1) All civilizations are male creations. (2) On the purely social order typifying truly primitive societies, civilizations grafted systems of *political* organization. (3) The essentially ethical tenor of primitive social life (some writers speak of its "magical," its "prelogical" or "emotional" atmosphere) is augmented with, and complemented by, a distinctly *rational* order. *All civilizations are based on rationality of greater or lesser validity.* (4) Granted, then, that civilization represents a male phase within the larger evolutionary rhythms of human evolution, that it is based on sex-linked characters, new as compared with essentially feminine primitivity, it follows that civilization, directly or indirectly, is genetically conditioned, because sex itself has a genetic foundation. The concept of mental speciation thus becomes as legitimate as that of anatomical speciation, though it must be understood that the two are not congruous. Mental speciation took place within biological.

The basic similarity of biological and mental speciation, i.e., the genetic origin of both, is apparent from the circumstance that both begin with a single, or a few, individual(s) in which the requisite genetic complexes first appear. Both gain ground by means of the propagation of these mutations through a population, augmented, probably, by the spontaneous rise of like, or equally valuable, mutations in other individuals.

As regards mental speciation, this throws light on a number of important facts. First, the tribes, races and individuals which never reached the stage of civilization are obviously those in whom the necessary mutations never arose. Second, it explains why without exception in early recorded history, each civilization and its political institutions, power and wealth represent, as it were, exclusive "patent rights" of a small dominant minority, the creators or "inventors" of civilization. Third, it also explains why, the qualities making for civilization being sex-linked, even the women of the ruling class never contributed anything to the material and spiritual wealth of early civilizations and why to this day they have by and large remained on the receiving end. Exactly because of its genetic foundation, because it rests on mental speciation, civilization was bound to constitute a class, i.e., species, privilege far into historic times. Certainly in early history whether a man belonged to "class" or "mass" was determined by his genetic constitution, and even regarding much later times it remains fallacious to identify civilizations with entire races or whole populations. They were never anything but concomitants of mental speciation *within* a race or people, of the "political species" that diverged from the more primitive and "purely social" ancestral species still constituting the mass under the ruling class. (The gradual blurring of this distinction will be dealt with in Chapter 12.)

The details of the genesis of civilizations are still far from sufficiently elucidated. The paramount difficulty is of course that the psychological development subtending the genesis of civilizations has left us no fossils, no palpable rudiments, and that a comparative anatomy of human genetic complexes is still a mere hope. Nevertheless, the rise of political civilizations is so obviously an aspect of human evolution, one can hardly go wrong in applying general evolutionary theory to this special domain. After all, even the psychic manifestations of man are manifestations of his genetic and epigenetic system in their interactions with the environment.

They are largely behavioral aspects, and these constitute a very important side of evolutionary science.

The following cannot claim to be more than a sketchy outline of what I believe may someday pave the way toward a fuller understanding of civilizational genesis. For the benefit of those not conversant with modern evolutionary theory, I shall single out a few of the important evolutionary principles in quotations from a most authoritative, very recent and monumental survey of the field, Professor Ernst Mayr's *Animal Species and Evolution*,[1] and try to show how closely, *mutatis mutandis*, they apply to the "mental speciation" apparent in the rise of civilizations. The whole matter is, after all, merely a new phase in the development of the organism-environment complementarity.

The first step toward speciation generally is a change in the genetic constitution of a few members of an existing species. That civilization, as a new masculine behavioral mode, i.e., a sex-linked phenomenon, also is genetically conditioned has already been mentioned. History knows of no female civilizations.

"Speciation is potentially a process of evolutionary rejuvenation. . . . The importance of speciation is that it invites experimentation. . . . Speciation is a progressive, not a retrogressive, process" (Mayr, p. 555). Nothing could illustrate this better than the differences between the mental genus Primitivity and the mental genus Civilization. All primitive societies are ancient, hoary, weary, caught in sterile routines and sterile mental concepts. In the process of civilizational speciation the key words are enterprise, progress, experimentation, exploration, a search for the new. Rising civilizations are imbued with the spirit of youth.

"An incipient species can complete the process of speciation only if it can find a previously unoccupied niche" (Mayr, p. 574). As indicated, I see the deciding factor for the origin of civilization in the genetically conditioned advance into *a new mental habitat*, a new spiritual environment, from the predominantly ethico-biological or magical sphere of primitivity into the overwhelmingly rational one typical of civilization.

"In order to be able to enter a new niche or adaptive zone successfully, a species must be preadapted for it" (Mayr, p. 593). The various "mental species" responsible for the origin of civilizations undoubtedly were. It cannot be an accident that the new, rational environment was the discovery of members of the sex by nature less tied than the female to the ethico-biological climate of primitivity.

"During the shift into a new adaptive zone, one structure or structural complex is usually under particularly strong selection pressure. . . . This structure or complex then evolves very rapidly while all others lag behind. As a result there is not a steady or harmonious change of all parts of the 'type,' " but a rather spotty, "mosaic" evolution (Mayr, p. 598). Likewise, much that touches us as primitive survived among the ruling classes of all civilizations. All developed "spottily," "mosaically," with an overemphasis on rationality.

"Habitat shifts of a minor nature . . . require little special preadaptation and have little evolutionary potential. At the other extreme are shifts of fundamental significance such as those from aquatic to terrestrial, or from terrestrial to aerial life. Such shifts are possible only to the possessor of a highly unlikely combination of characteristics and this is the reason for the infrequency of such shifts" (Mayr, p. 593). It is also the reason why among the thousands of primitive tribes only a score have advanced to civilized life.

"Not every evolutionary experiment is a success; in fact most of them are failures" (Mayr, p. 595). The bearing on civilizational experiments is obvious.

"The interaction between organism and environment is the most important single determinant in the rise and fall of evolutionary types" (Mayr, p. 617). In human social evolution the dominant environment is always man himself. In the genesis of civilizations the "most important single determinant" is an entirely new attitude of the founders toward the rest of their fellowmen, resulting in the dichotomy of "class" and "mass," rulers and subjects, masters and slaves. Slavery is part of all early civilizations.

Variants of existing biological species, in order to become true species, depend on "isolating mechanisms," geographical, ecological or behavioral isolation (Mayr, pp. 89–109, 484, 493). Early political man consciously erected rigid class barriers in order to develop into, and maintain himself as, a distinct mental species.

Many more such correspondences could be pointed out. But we need not depend altogether on a comparison of the principles of organic and mental speciation to support the thesis of the genetic origin of civilization. An even better case can be made on the evidence of behavioral evolution. In biological as in mental speciation a new habitat of necessity elicits a new behavior. The essential differences between primitive and civilized man are behavioral, and politics merely represents a new chapter in the phylogeny of human male behavior in a "new species."

Basically, behavior is genetically determined, that is, instinctive, and hence also part of the overall picture of speciation. Here I would, therefore, propound the thesis that, as an aspect of mental speciation originally confined to the male sex, civilization represents essentially a modification of, and a development from, male "display" behavior. "Display" refers to that often extravagant "showing off" of the male animal, either vis-à-vis the coveted female or a potential male rival. In the animal world this "display," or, as the German ethologists call it, more characteristically, "*das Imponiergehaben,*" is either pure "boasting" concerning the male's brawn, or it takes the form (among birds, e.g.) of a gorgeous display of color, of form and size of feathers, or all these elements combined. All this is of course unconscious, instinctive, confined to the mating season or territorial defense.

With man, i.e., the archetype of political man, it became conscious and, since his readiness to mate and to fight is not seasonally restricted, it became permanent behavior. Above all, from starting as a mere showing-off of brawn, it became more and more blended with a display of *brain*. As an aspect of mental speciation it gradually became intellectualized. This, to my mind, is the beginning, e.g., of the human habit of dressing. Initially it was almost certainly "dressing-up"; it was *Imponiergehaben,* a primitively sophisticated way of impressing the women and those among the males who were not so clever, those who remained "primitives." Also, it was no doubt a way of gaining *power* over them, magical power. The feathered headgear of Indian chiefs, war paint and gaudy blankets may represent the initial stage of this development.[2]

Such, then, was probably the chief behavioral aspect of mental speciation in its beginnings. And no doubt it remained for a long time confined to this sort of elementary "show business," for even today the primitives among us, especially women, the shady underworld of males and the nouveaux riches, can conceive of no other way to indicate their readiness to become part of civilization than "dolling up," "sharp" dressing and other extravagant ornamentation of their anatomy. Only very, very gradually such display became intellectualized, but even then it remained in its brainier stages essentially a way of "showing off." It remained ostentation, as is especially obvious among oriental peoples, whether it took the form of ever more gaudy clothing, the use of crowns and jewels, or whether it finally took the form of pyramids, obelisks, magnificent temples and palaces—outside of which the world generally remained arrested in stark primitivity and squalor.

Ever since these quasi-animalic origins of civilization, *Power* has made the most extensive use of every form of ostentation to keep the plebs in awe. And today, the more primitive among us still succumb to it, even clamor for it, be it in the form of fancy-dress statesmanship, royal and military pomp, or fancy-dress religion.

Even after these "displays" had advanced to a truly intellectual stage, they still predominantly served the purpose of emphasizing power. The art of writing remained for a long time a magic art, the beginnings of astronomy are inseparable from astrology, and even we have not forgotten that "knowledge is power." Here is one of those characteristic examples of "mosaic" development:

civilized rationality coupled to the primitive magic concept of power, which has lost all meaning in modern basic science.

MATRIARCHY AND PATRIARCHY

Civilization, then, means the supersedure of a primitive, purely social, mammalian-matronal order of life by a more purely mental order under the dominance of a small group of "new males," the political men.

Among primitive societies there have been found a number of cases of the almost unalloyed mammalian family in which the male has no place. Even where the men became integrated into the maternal order, the position of the women generally remained supreme. This state of things, together with certain vestiges of "higher primitivity" carried over into civilizations, has led a number of students to postulate a universal prehistoric age during which women ruled the world. The best-known among these is the Swiss legal philosopher J. J. Bachofen.[3] It is evident, though, that the Matriarchal Theory,[4] as it is called, owed much to the inability of the Victorian Age to visualize a world in which the state did not exist yet.

An illuminating borderline case of nonpolitical matriarchy is presented by the Iroquois Indians.[5] In matters purely social the matrons were the masters, arranging marriages and owning all the land and the habitations. They dominated and directed even some of the most important ceremonial organizations; indeed, they nominated candidates if vacancies arose in the council of the chiefs and they could admonish and impeach elected chiefs. However, no woman ever held a seat in the supreme council of the Iroquois League. Political organization was still in its earliest beginnings, but typically and completely in the hands of the men—even if as a matter of sheer ancient prestige the matrons indulged in a sort of political backseat driving. That means, the old matronal order was still intact. It was in fact never displaced, but something new was about to be *superimposed* on it, and this new thing was *political organization* created by the males.

The foundations of social life, then, as the direct development from the mammalian family, were evidently laid by women, whereas the political superstructures are masculine inventions, and each sex has, by and large, retained dominance over the realm of its creation.

The shift from matriarchal "socialism" to paternal "politicalism" meant, or at least made possible, the ascent of that vast cliff separating primitivity from civilization (with a number of transitory stages which we must here neglect). No change in human history has had such far-reaching consequences. It represented an evolutionary leap as radical in a way as that from inanimate matter to life or from the plant kingdom to the animal kingdom. Only in political civilization do we finally see coming into its own the ultimate expression of the dynamic-animalic principle: systematic thought.

By no means was it a change affecting only the surface of human life. Its influence was felt in the deepest recesses of existence. As always, in the sudden appearance and the rapid expansion of new forms of life in evolution, the new could not establish itself without displacing some parts of the old order. In the Great Revolution with which we are concerned, this is nowhere better apparent than in the field of religion, which here furnishes classical proof that, contrary to all claims of its professional caretakers, it is never anything absolute, rarely embodies eternal values, but is chiefly one of the psychic mirrors reflecting prevailing cultural standards.

One of the universal symbols of primitive peoples is the Great Mother, goddess of fertility, of the fruitful earth, the giver of birth, supreme embodiment of the female dominance of life. But wherever a human society rose to the level of political civilization, the Great Mother was superseded by masculine gods. She either had to clear the field altogether, or descend to a minor niche in the arsenal of divinities—as the goddess of venery and prostitution, for instance, like Aphrodite-Venus. The supreme deities of all great historic civilizations were without exception created in the image of the male, they were all deifications of the "new" male who created civilization: Amon-Re, Yahweh, Assur, Ahura-Mazda, Zeus, Odin, Allah. And their priests and prophets are men, no longer women, as was the case under the supremacy of the Great Mother.

Another typical feature of some early civilizations is the retreat of woman in the daily life in favor of the male and her loss of prestige, often her complete moral and intellectual devaluation. At the dawn of Greek history, for example, as it is reflected in its myths and legends, its epic poems and part of the classical drama, women still played prominent roles and stood in high regard. Homer's *Iliad* glorifies a war fought over a woman (something the classical Greeks would have considered supremely ridiculous). In the everyday life of the same classical age, which still drew its poetic subjects from the old legendary well, the women, however, had become reduced to shadowy household fixtures. The more the pronounced dynamism of politically oriented civilization allowed the men to dominate, the more the very concept of woman became, for a time at least, degraded to the lowest level. In certain of Plato's dialogues she appears as the incarnation of the basest sensuality, almost an animal still wholly instinct-ridden, whereas man stands as the incarnation of the loftiest spirit. "Great Zeus," says the hero of Euripides' play *Hippolytus*, "why didst thou, to man's sorrow, put woman, evil counterfeit, to dwell where shines the sun?"

Nor stand the Greeks alone in this regard. Elsewhere, too, the emergence of masculine civilization made woman the embodiment of everything degrading, even of sin. The myth of Eve's apple and the snake put the brunt of the guilt for human misery and the expulsion from paradise on woman. This was quite perverse, considering that it was the men who had broken out of the primeval Eden; but in the mood they now were in, it was obviously convenient to blame all trouble on the women. Making the maternal sex the scapegoat for everything that went wrong in this new budding world of masculinity became, in fact, one of the chief articles of creed of some of the new religions.

It is from sin come into the world through Eve that Judaism and, even more, early Christianity desired to save humanity.[6] Saint Paul, the inveterate bachelor, is the classical incarnation of this male naïveté. His derogatory attitude toward woman became the official attitude of the Church. Salvation became a purely masculine affair because it was largely salvation by bachelors from woman, the personification in the mind of the upstart male of everything base and pointing back to a stagnant past from which he had just escaped, and in which his position had probably been rather humiliating. The fervent religious dream of salvation was essentially a sort of evolutionary male backbiting.

Obviously, then, the view cannot be discarded that at, or just before, the dawn of recorded history a profound upheaval took place in some branches of the human species, a revolution without par, tantamount to the superseding of the female by the male as the dominant element in the world. This is in perfect agreement with the large rhythms, the slow oscillations between static and dynamic phases in the evolution of life, and with the basic architectural pattern of the physical world as a whole.

Woman was bound to dominate primitive life because it was essentially family life, and the family, as well as primitive culture, were in the main her creation. But the male was bound to ascend to dominance in civilization because it is his handiwork.

The age of matriarchy is as much a sociobiological certainty as it is a piece of political fiction.

11

PRIMITIVITY AND CIVILIZATION

BEFORE we proceed to look deeper into the explosive rise of an order of masculine dominance, the most recent "wave" in evolution, two fundamental questions require attention.

(1) Why did primitivity last so long?

(2) What was the precise position of the male under the matriarchal dispensation?

We shall take them up in this order.

PROBLEMS OF PRIMITIVITY

In recent years we have witnessed a spate of fascinating publications on monkeys and apes, all with the same result—that they cannot tell us anything about the unique position of man, except by contrast. Nor can we learn much from the first African deviates from monkeydom, which now are reckoned to have lived two million years ago. The great value of these discoveries is that they have enormously drawn out the road we traveled. If we have any human sense, they should ultimately deflate what theoretical optimism we may ever have possessed, whether as socialists, communists, social engineers, humanitarians or Great-Societeers. If it took two million years to convert us into the imperfect half-apes we still are in some regards, the conclusion cannot be farfetched that the Millennium is not just around the corner, whether or not

159

we know which corner. No civilization ever reached "the corner."
But perhaps this very fact might engender the ambition to be the
first to reach it, which would certainly have to be by means other
than those so far tried by our predecessors.

Yet, considering the entire length of the evolution of life, even
the two million years of our human "separatist movement" appear
like a veritable catapulting out of the world of the "instinct tunnels" into that of an open mind, a radically new environment
replete with new problems. This, no doubt, required a great deal
of time for readaptation, for groping, testing and experimenting.

In this new, uncharted, mental world, nature's guiding lines
were lacking, or at least not obvious; they had to be discovered.
Here rules of conduct were not prescribed by physiology and
neural anatomy, but had to be consciously devised. In other words,
the transfer meant no less than the revolutionary change from a
strictly biological, i.e., instinctive, orientation to a moral one. And
if two million years seem a long apprenticeship to us, we should
remember that not even we have fully learned the lesson.

In general, the learning process was the salient feature of this
new, mental, environment. For what one generation had managed
to convey to memory or embedded in habit was not automatically
passed on to its descendants through genetic methods. Everything
had to be learned anew by each generation. This called for the
development of means of mental communication, above all,
spoken language. What vestiges of animal "language" may have
been carried over from the lower primate level offered little help,
for it was inborn sign language of the biological sphere, whereas
all human languages are abstract symbolic languages without
parallel in the animal world (if we disregard the "language" of
bees). All apes can understand all other apes' instinctive signs,
whereas human languages, as invented, abstract systems, are like
secret codes understood only by the "ins" of a certain cultural
circle. The evolution of spoken language alone should suffice to
make us understand the necessity for an enormously long and
relatively vegetative period of development. It was an immense
task for an animal to learn to be human.

Language offers perhaps the most convincing testimony to the effect that it was woman, not the male of the species, who gave primitivity its deepest imprint. Even if we had no surviving primitive tribes, we could not avoid this conclusion. Language—which undoubtedly evolved from once-instinctive mother-offspring communication—is woman's greatest gift to the species, and every single people on earth pays her that tribute, for nowhere do we find paternal languages, but only mother tongues.[1] Spoken language has become the essence of humanity, and its possession alone might explain why Homo sapiens, even at his first appearance in fossil records, has approximately the same brain capacity as modern man.

Of no less weight in any attempt to understand the slow development of primitivity under female dominance is another factor.[2] As in some insect societies—ants and bees, but not termites—so in earliest human primitivity, the males may not have been fully, or not always, part of the actual social order, but outsiders and merely tolerated. Traces of this state of things have survived to this day. The "real people" among such primitive tribes is composed of the maternal families, whereas the adult males live in a separate village, or a separate communal establishment. As outsiders and mere biological functionaries needed to assure the continuance of "womankind," they have little opportunity to contribute anything of significance to the social order proper. Maternal families without a male "head" are still common among our Negro population, each child often having a different father.

This still leaves us with the problem why civilization did not arise as soon as the men became integrated into the matriarchal families. For one thing, the requisite genetic constitutions may not have appeared for a long time, or if they did, were premature and hence discriminated against, as ideas far ahead of their time may invoke punishment on their originators. For another thing, the process of integration may have been much slower than is generally believed. This surmise comes from students of Indo-European languages, who suggest that the original meaning of

father was probably not, as today, "progenitor," but "protector."
In other words, the "man of the family" at first may have been no
more than a sort of hired man or majordomo, possibly taken on
in times of danger or migration to guard mother and children. This
would have furnished a natural starting point for his more complete integration, his becoming permanent mate and sire of all
of a woman's offspring.

But it remains questionable whether this same line of development was followed by other human races possessing biparental
families. We come nearer to an acceptable solution if we disregard
external factors and look at the problem as one of psychosomatic
development, which of course is not independent of genetic
changes. For it is virtually certain that the biological evolution of
Homo sapiens did not come to an abrupt and final termination
with his appearance. Psychosocial evolution itself was bound to
provide feedbacks affecting even the physical heritage of the
species.

THE RELATIVITY OF SEX

Nowhere is there a hard and fast division between the sexes. The
majority of plants are bisexed, and in the lower animal kingdom
hermaphroditism is common (earthworms, snails, etc.). With a
certain marine worm (*Bonellia viridis*) all free-swimming larvae
are females, and only those that manage to settle as parasites on
the long proboscis of an old female gradually turn into males.
With numerous fishes and birds, every individual of either sex can
potentially display either male or female behavior (e.g., an inferior male confronting a superior male will show the behavior of
a female, while a superior female will behave like a male opposite
an inferior sister). Even among mammals the dividing line is
never absolute. Billy goats as well as primitive human males with
functional mammary glands have been known. In a sense, every
man is still part woman and every woman part man. The final
outcome of ontogenesis depends on such delicate factors that in

the same individual anatomical and psychic sex do not necessarily agree. The effeminate man is as frequent as is the virago.

Moreover, the frequency of parthenogenesis in the lower animal kingdom allows us to regard the female as the primary sex, the male as the secondary. Males certainly are never reproductively autonomous, whereas many females are. A few years ago a medical release from England had it that even among humans virgin birth need not always be relegated to the land of myth. The concept of the secondary sex might in part explain why to this day the physical and psychic development of the human male tends to be slower than that of the female. This generic trait suggests that during the infancy of the species mentally fully mature persons may have been found only among the matrons, whereas all males remained "children"—an observation which belongs to the stock in trade of novelistic and dramatic heroines even of our day. This condition may have lasted for hundreds of thousands of years and would explain why male civilizations appeared so late. If we take further into account that the discovery of paternity is a very recent event in the history of the species (as late as the beginning of our century some primitive groups were not yet aware of it), we have every reason to believe that for ages the social position of the human male was rather precarious, that he seemed devoid of purpose and was perhaps considered an unessential appendage to womankind. By contrast, the maternal function of woman was never in doubt and always assured her a dominant position in primitive circumstances.

Erich Neumann,[3] an Israeli psychologist who has especially studied the earliest phase of the evolution of the human psyche, points out that on primitive levels "the male . . . is beloved as a child and youth and used an an instrument of fertilization," but he "remains an integral part of the female" and is "never recognized in his intrinsic masculinity, his male specificity." One may well go further. There is the great likelihood of a time when the male *could not* contribute anything significantly masculine to society because he was not sufficiently differentiated, either physically or mentally, from the female and was probably less mature. Darwin pointed out that some of the primitive human strains he observed showed remarkably little difference between the sexes, a condition which is widespread throughout the animal kingdom.

Civilization, as was stressed in the foregoing chapter, is simply the result of the discovery of a new, hitherto unoccupied, environment and the exploration of its novel potentialities. It is a male discovery, the requisite for which was a peculiar, genetically determined predisposition, a new, though not necessarily higher, mentality. To repeat: the prevailing mentality among primitives is of an ethical nature, rooted in the intense consciousness of blood relationship; whereas civilization is essentially based on the discovery of rational logic by the sex less preoccupied with purely biological problems than were the primitive matrons.

Not until the male sex had psychically diverged to an appreciable degree from the female, or at least a critical percentage of such "new" males was present in a society, could the latter emerge on the scene of history as a civilization with a dynamic masculine orientation and masculine leadership. Such leadership, however, remained confined to activities in the "new environment" of dynamic rational thought. Certainly, during the earliest phases civilization was merely *superimposed* on the old matriarchal order, which usually continued in its established ways as if nothing had happened.

It is worth giving a passing thought here to the fact that, so far as we know, hardly any primitive society has ever vanished from the face of the earth by simply expiring. Such primitive orders as are not yet assimilated into civilization have apparently existed almost since the appearance of man, whereas no civilization has outlived four thousand years. There can be no doubt that the difference is accounted for by the difference between ethical and rational social organization. Now there is always a certain rational element innate in ethic, which makes an ethically organized society in the fullest sense a complementarity of "harmonious opposites" and thus allows it to endure indefinitely. On the other hand, civilizations have usually attempted to make rationality absolute in their own novel spheres. To use a popular expression, they have generally been "too clever for their own good" and hence short-lived.

We shall return to this problem again in later chapters. Our next task is to illustrate that civilization actually *is* the supersedure of a purely social order by a political one or, in basic physical terms, a "protonic" by an "electronic" one. All is not accidental in civilization: certain fundamental principles are involved even here. To show this is one of the aims of this work.

EGYPT, GREECE AND ROME

The best-known of the early history makers, the rulers of Egypt,[4] strike us in many ways as almost modern. They were virile, indomitable in the face of the most formidable climatic and geophysical obstacles, marvelously creative, and from the beginning given to the worship of deifications of masculinity. The god who finally achieved supremacy among these was Re, the Sun God, conqueror of the night and of the moon (usually a female symbol in primitivity), the god of creation who brings fruitfulness and life to earth and can overcome death. Most characteristically, however, Re the Sun God of heaven worked the miracle of overcoming death only in favor of those who could *pay the price*, those fortunate few who had the wherewithal, that is, the creative spirit which could procure the premium demanded by the god and which alone could save man from becoming a victim of death.

The great evolutionary significance here lies in the fact that Re the Sun God (in earlier times and in different regions of the country known as Horus and later as Amon or Amon-Re) was from the beginning *a political god*, the supreme deity *only* of his earthly counterparts, the terrestrial "lords of creation," the "new males," originators of statesmanship and inventors of political civilization. Certainly during the Old Kingdom he was exclusively the god of the ruling class and a stranger to the subject populace.

It was this assertive, revolutionary class of worshipers and protégés of a supreme male deity who from the beginning monopolized all power. It was they who, defying the progressive desiccation of the once-fertile North African grasslands, refused to retreat to more amenable southern regions; who, instead, descended into the treacherous marshes of the Nile and by means of canals and dams converted them into an earthly paradise. It was they who, besides canals and dams, built all the other wonders of Egypt, palaces, temples and—with some justification, we must admit—monuments to themselves.

The creators of Egyptian civilization and the originators of politics and statesmanship were one. They were the first "complete males" in history, bringing to dominance the dynamic animal principle as a new means of social organization: the principle of *authority*, of *power*, of self-affirmation.

Primitive female dominance was always passive. Its supreme organizing principle was based on the ethics of *piety*, that is, the awareness of the physiological bonds between mother and offspring. This minor key of life continued its sway unabated in the large subject populace over whom the creators of Egyptian civilization had made themselves lords. The rulers knew marriage, that is, paternity, whereas among the subjects matrimony appears to have been unknown for a long time. In the subject population, property, especially land, still descended from mother to daughter, in the old tradition of matriarchal primitivity[5]; among the rulers it passed from father to son, though even here we find vestiges of matriarchy surviving in that the Pharaoh's rule became legitimate only through his marriage to the heir direct according to the old order of things—his sister.

Many of the deities of the subject class still were feminine, and even some of their male gods remained predominantly feminine in their attributes. The god who finally rose to the highest position among them was Osiris, the spirit of the slumbering earth, of night and of vegetative fecundity, in essence, therefore, still a passive female deity. More important: Osiris was also the ruler of the dead, those whom life had left behind. These primitive masses witnessed the rise in their midst of something entirely new in human life, a civilization; but they were themselves hardly part of it. Being what they were, they could not be really part of it, just as the animals they kept could by their nature be no part of it. Life had left them behind, and the awareness of having fallen behind found symbolic form in the image of their highest deity, Osiris.

In the supreme gods of the two strata of earliest Egypt we thus find strikingly personified the old and the new order of life: in Osiris the dormant shadowland of a nonpolitical life of prehistoric primitivity dominated by the vegetative-maternal principle; and in the Sun God Re the splendors of a political civilization conjured up by the inventive, creative spiritual powers of the new "complete" male. So, at this point in the flux of time we stand as on a great divide, looking backward on the dull uneventful darkness of somnolescent matriarchy, and forward toward the fireworks and the turbulence of masculine history.

A picture similar in essence to that of Egypt with its two strata is presented by ancient Greece, except that here we find the old and the new order epitomized in two cities: female-dominated Sparta and male-dominated Athens. Separated by only ninety miles of airspace, the two lived worlds, millennia, apart. Athens during her brief florescence, the Athens that was, in the words of Thucydides, "the education of Hellas," the sculptor's, architect's, philosopher's, poet's and dramatist's paradise, this Athens, as was already mentioned, saw women virtually vanish from the scene of life to be caged in narrowest domesticity. It was the Athenian men who filled the air with a glory that finally shed its light over the Mediterranean and has lasted to this day.

If Athens was exclusively a man's world, how different was Sparta! This city—if city it could be called, for it was a mere camp—presented the curious spectacle of a community fossilized right on the threshold separating primitivity from civilization. It was a sort of civic Lot's wife turned into a pillar of bitter salt. Even Spartan masculinity had no more than just crossed the great threshold with its foremost toe. Whereas civilizations are almost all based on industries and trade, Sparta was still so essentially primitive and conservative as to forbid to its citizens all trade and the possession of coined money. The few crafts without which even Sparta could not do were hereditary family property. No matter how good a musician you were, you could not, according to Herodotus, become a flute player unless your father had been one, and your grandfather and great-grandfather before you.

More telling still was the condition of Spartan womanhood. The women were still the masters. Though formal marriage had become the rule, the institution meant little. According to some ancient historians, a majority of the population was, as the euphemism went, "virgin born," and there was no insistence that children born to a married woman be her husband's children. As in some very primitive societies, the men of Sparta ate and slept in separate communal establishments. Private homes were for women and children. Marital relations could be maintained only by stealth, and under this system it probably made little difference to what bed a Spartan warrior sneaked under cover of night. The henpecked Spartans were the laughingstock of Athens, and there is more than a little suspicion that their exclusive specialization in militarism and war for war's sake had its cause in the inability of their unimaginative minds to think of other ways to get away from their females. The brutal tyranny which they maintained over all their conquests, the proverbial insolence and misbehavior of the Spartans beyond their bailiwick, were magnified reflections of the way they were treated at home at the hands of their women. A large part of the power of Spartan matrons was derived from their hold on the land—another survival of matriarchy.

The worst was that Sparta's womanhood was not only prehistoric, but obstinately so, defiantly anarchistic in their refusal to recognize the law because it had no precedent in the older feminine world order. In their diehards' revolt against the newfangled notions of the men, these women became termagants and tyrannized the males worse than men could have done. The men had taken the first timid step in the direction of a civilization under the rule of law, the women rebelled against it, sabotaged it and, triumphing, continued to wield the big stick over their semi-civilized men. But, asked Aristotle, "what difference does it make whether women rule, or the rulers are ruled by women?"[6]

Athens in time became a community of men of the world and a beacon for ages to come, but in the cultural history of Greece Sparta remained a mere flatulence, inspiring in later ages only to totalitarians and militarists. To Athens goes the signal honor of being the first nation in history to whom freedom became a political ideal, who sought constitutional means to insure freedom and to attain ever more freedom. To Sparta the very notion of freedom remained revolting. Brutal martial discipline was her civic ideal.

The situation during the earliest days of Rome closely resembles that of awakening Egypt, with the old and the new orders personified in two social strata of different ethnic origins and differing religions. The actual founders and earliest rulers of Rome (i.e., the walled city as distinguished from the prior conglomic of open villages) were Etruscan conquerors, political-minded establishing their lordship over a group of vegetating Latin peasants. The expulsion of the Etruscan royal house, the Tarquinians (ca. 500 B.C.), in no way affected this situation, for the Etruscan nobles merely converted the former one-man absolutism of the king to a corporate class absolutism. The corporate name which they gave themselves and cherished—the Patricians—at least seems to suggest that they were men proud of the knowledge of who their fathers were. For their social order was based on a high and deeply religious concept of marriage and the paternal family. Among them, marriage was an exalted religious ceremony and such a sacred class privilege as to be in the very earliest days of Rome strictly forbidden to the subject class of the Plebeians, in whose primordial order the relations of the sexes were apparently not yet well regulated. The ruling Patricians, on the other hand, clearly realized the enormous importance of the legalized paternal family, and no small part of their might and political inspiration flowed from this source. The only ones with legitimate families, within which their powers were absolute, they were also the exclusive possessors of political rights and might. The patriarchal family was the epitome of politics, and as such was treated as a class prerogative, much as dominant classes of other ages treated cavalry service, education, or the right to vote. Only much later, as the result of a number of revolutions, was the Patriciate opened to prominent members of what once had been the prehistoric and nonpolitical Plebeians. But even this did not materially alter the basic situation, the stark difference between a ruling class with proprietary political rights and powers and a politically disfranchised subject populace.

Roman history and civilization, like that of Egypt and Athens, is distinctly the expression of a self-assertive masculinity, something quite unimaginable under prehistoric conditions of vegetative matriarchalism. In the case of Rome, nothing could offer clearer testimony to this than the amazing fact that the very ex   e of femininity was unknown to the earliest Roman law.

    .archalism never knew law, it knew only custom; so why ..ould the law, a masculine invention, trouble to take notice of the sex that had nothing to do with its inception? There was logic in that. The law was for men only because it was strictly the upshot of the revolutionary rational order of dynamic, political masculinity.

12

BASIC CIVILIZATIONAL PROBLEMS

I N Chapter 10 attention was drawn to the fundamental morphological fact of the world's constitution that protonic-static-vegetative-female phases of evolution expand essentially in the "horizontal," whereas electronic-dynamic-animalic-male phases display a remarkable tendency to develop in the "vertical" dimension. By its very nature as an essentially "horizontal" phenomenon with practically no gradient, primitivity could neither "fall" nor slide back and hence could endure almost forever. By contrast, civilizations, as essentially "vertical" developments, include in their very nature the possibility of a "fall." The evolutionary casualties among the genus Civilization have indeed been phenomenal.

To a large extent, to be sure, the problematics of political civilizations are based in their extreme evolutionary youth, their being still in the very beginning of the experimental stage. Civilizational mortality is infant mortality. Within the entire span of life of two to three billion years civilizations occupy no more than six thousand years. Translated into time dimensions more easily grasped, that would mean approximately the last fifth of a second of a twenty-four-hour day. No civilization has been more than a "flash in the pan" of life. The reason may well be that, in fundamental terms, civilizations, as was said before, represent an advance into an entirely novel and hitherto unoccupied habitat, that of rational thought, but that before long their affairs were usually taken over by instinctive animal drives. The fall of almost every civilization has been the triumph of rationalized atavistic instincts over the ethico-rational mind. All the traditional mystification about extinct civilizations merely glosses over the fact that atavistic incompetents were "monkeying" with a mental world beyond their understanding.

In this chapter we shall consider only a few of the basic phenomena distinguishing political civilization from social primitivity. They should further heighten our awareness of the fact that even complex civilizations are not purely accidental or artificial phenomena, and that survival and continued development is possible only on the foundation of age-old principles.

STRATIFICATION

The term "stratification," generally used for a certain aspect of social morphology, is merely another word for the more fundamental "complementarity." Wherefore, since complementarity itself is the primal form of the social principle, an unstratified, classless society is a contradiction in terms, an impossibility. Even primitive societies are to some extent stratified according to sex, age, and certain very specialized activities already to be found among them: priestly functions, the arts, the committing to memory of the unwritten traditions, myths, history, and the innumerable details of the social code.

In civilizations complementary stratification becomes highly multiplex because of the immense functional diversity. But what chiefly distinguishes civilizations from primitive societies is the novel dichotomy of *rulers* and *subjects*. This main stratification is actually synonymous with early civilization. Perhaps it was coeval with the transition from nomadism to settled agricultural conditions and no doubt imperative where the shift was from steppes to such marshes as originally occupied the valley of the Nile, that of the two rivers of Mesopotamia and the Yellow River of China. The transformation of these marshes into habitable and arable land called for enormous manpower which, we may be sure, was not willingly furnished by former herdsmen and hunters.

We find the institution of slavery an integral part of every arising civilization, and nothing could better illustrate than slavery that civilization meant an advance into the new mental habitat of rational thought. The small group of "new males," the discoverers of authoritarian power, could not but look down upon those who had not experienced their "change of mind" with the same cool rational detachment characteristic of their reactions vis-à-vis the physical environment which, the first humans to do so, they set out to conquer and transform. They were indeed a new human species. *They knew* they were a new species, immortal gods after death, and the highest of them, the kings, were revered as gods even in their lifetime. Even the Roman emperors were still held to be gods.[1] The rationality of this may seem fallacious to us, but rationality it was and unknown to primitivity. Were not the achievements of these "new men" godlike, when compared with those of primitives? Did not the earth itself obey their will? Did they not, like gods, create new worlds, paradises out of marshes and deserts? Who would not under the circumstances hold himself akin to the gods?

It is a long way from this earliest historic age of slave-keeping god-kings to modern democracy with its belief in the freedom and equality of all. If we adhere to the scientific view of the unity of the human organism in its physical as well as its mental aspects, we cannot, as is commonly done, regard the change as a mere "change of customs." We must rather look upon it as a concomitant of certain organic changes in the majority of men, finally culminating in the realization that, no matter how intricately the body politic became subdivided, all classes are equally necessary. In other words, even sociopolitical thought rose to the insight of complementarity, though generally using different terminologies. For in every society classes and strata are complementary aspects of a whole and none can exist without the others.

Modern population genetics would seem to furnish the best

theoretical basis for any attempt to elucidate these evolutionary transmutations. Now, the assumption that the genesis of civilizations is to be found in "mental speciation" implies that the "parent species" remained temporarily arrested and became the primitive mass of slaves or serfs of the small civilized "daughter species." This primitive mass comprised not only the vast majority of the males but, strictly speaking, the entire female sex as well. No matter how abhorrent slavery may seem to us today, it is completely unrealistic to regard its origin, as untutored radicals like to do, as a mere conspiracy of a small clique against the "mass." It bears repeating that it was, on the contrary, the "show" of novel, sex-linked, genetic complexes possessed only by the "new species," the small, dominant minority. It was inevitable, because natural, as may be gathered from the fact that we meet the identical situation all over the world wherever civilizations arose.

However, genetic changes similar to those which led to the rise of the first dominant class could at any time appear in the subject populace. At the same time a "gene flow" from the top to the bottom of the body politic undoubtedly always took place, chiefly through concubines and other extramarital liaisons. (It has been estimated that today every individual of Western or Central Western European stock may with equal probability count Charlemagne among his or her ancestors.) And, finally, it is known that genes can disappear from a population as unaccountably as they appear. All this led in the course of millennia to events which again can be observed in all civilizations on which we are sufficiently informed. First, creativity can forsake a ruling stratum, in which case, if the rulers succeed in clinging to their powers, civilizations ossify or perish. Second, on the basis of new genetic changes stratification may also take place in the subject mass, one part of it remaining primitive, another part turning into a middle class. And from the middle class with its own typical mentality may arise concepts offering potentials for new social orders, new ways of dominance.

The following may be called the natural stages in the evolution of political structures: (1) political tribalism, which often represents little more than the old matriarchal order, plus a superordinate elementary masculine organization; (2) the order of royalty and nobility, usually developing into a feudal system, as it is familiar from Egypt, Japan and European history; (3) the commercial or bourgeois order, in which we ourselves are living. For the sake of completeness be it mentioned also that we ourselves are now witnesses of an incipient new order, the dawn of a scientific civilization and the beginning conflicts between the scientific spirit and pure commercialism, the attempts of the "old guard" to enslave science for its own, by now rather atavistic, ends.[2] (This subject will be taken up in Chapters 14 and 15.)

Now what is significant in this succession of "new ways of life," is that the older orders generally persist in secondary or lower tiers, either in their original or a modified form, functionally (like the once-dominant priesthoods) or rudimentarily (like royalty and nobility). Class distinctions may continue to be observed (as in England), or they may yield to a so-called classless society which, however, remains functionally as much stratified as any other, though shifts from one class to another are frequent. (A. N. Whitehead, in one of his reminiscences, refers to "the rule" that in England the surnames and descendants of the medieval barons are now to be found chiefly among the agricultural workers.)

There remains still to be considered the main question of this subchapter: how did the rigid dichotomy of masters and slaves become so blurred as to engender the modern doctrine of the equality of all men? The main reason, no doubt, is that the gene pools of populations, the totality of their genetic complexes, are never stagnant but in perpetual mixture and mutation, with new genes appearing, while others disappear, in every social stratum; thus in the course of centuries arise new mentalities, leading to a certain approximation of all classes and a modest fluidity in the social stratification.

But the genesis of "democratic" concepts, of the tenet of the equality of all before God and the law, was no doubt aided by

another factor, a trait which indeed all members of the biological
species Homo sapiens share. This is the gift of mimesis, or, more
generally, man's extraordinary capacity for learning, which of
course is nothing less than the faculty of imitation. As an inborn,
generic trait it has always formed the crucial link between biological heredity and social, i.e., learned, tradition. Imitation is
indeed the main pillar of tradition, the staunchest conservative
power. For the entire process of growing up, from infancy to
adulthood, and often beyond, is never anything but the emulation
of our "betters." Whether an individual just has intelligence
enough to learn to speak and in general to do as the others do, or
whether he becomes an expert mathematician, is merely a matter
of imitative degree—unless he becomes a creative mathematician
or a creative genius in some other field.

And who is not familiar with the fact that the imitator considers
himself as clever as the originator? "Why go to the trouble to
invent something new, for which nobody pays you, when it is
simpler and more profitable to imitate?" Here is probably the
deepest root of the doctrine of the equality of all. Through the
entire educational process, formal or informal, we become such
dyed-in-the-wool imitators, few ever dream of getting beyond this
stage. We can all of us use tools and machines which we would
never have the brains to devise, or play musical compositions,
which we could never write, on instruments beyond our inventive
ability. This rapprochement by way of imitation has always been
the greatest social equalizer, though it has left untouched the
original civilizational dichotomy between the creative "class" and
the "mass" of civilization's "maintenance crew" or, to use a more
genteel expression, the bearers of tradition.

Indeed, the mere imitators and guardians of traditions, in considering themselves the equals of inventors and discoverers, are not
far from an important evolutionary truth. For the fact is that any
novelty becomes effective in the advance of civilization only if it is
widely copied or imitated, and there is for this reason always an
intense selection pressure in favor of imitative ability. All innovations, like faculties acquired, become secure possessions only to the

degree to which they become routine, as every child who has just learned to ride a bicycle can attest. Thus, even in this exposed evolutionary domain we come back again to our most basic principle, the fact, namely, that all advancement depends on the complementarity of innovations and routines. Where there are no novelties to be imitated, societies stagnate, and if innovations, material or ideistic, find no followers, the result is the same. Both are equally important, and it is no doubt this realization, conscious or unconscious, which contributed very largely to the erosion of rigid class distinctions.

Nor was this realization at home only in sections of the lower classes. The ruling strata often shared it and hence found it expedient, or wise, or simply "humane" to impart some of their attainments and privileges to their inferiors. The application of the same laws to all, for instance, is a development due as much to a change of mind on the part of the masters as among their subjects.

In recent years literacy has been benevolently handed down to the masses who, as James Bryce[3] pointed out, even in nineteenth-century England were for the most part quite indifferent to the favor bestowed on them. They were equally doubtful regarding the gift of political rights which, again, they had never demanded. Both these cases may well be interpreted as indicating that even the masses were, as recently as a hundred years ago, conscious of constituting a separate mental species from the upper classes.

This brings up the question, to what extent can equalization be evolutionarily creative and at which point does it become a drag? For the truth remains that absolute equality is a mere doctrine without any natural basis. Without factual inequalities among men no civilization would ever have arisen, and existing civilizations would dissolve into chaos. For all evolution is the elaboration of complementarity, and this latter always involves asymmetry, the "harmony of opposites," the integration of unequals—equals cannot be integrated, only added up.

Consider, for instance, compulsory education from this point of view. It raises a demand for teachers far beyond what the spontaneous demand from below would call for and often leads to what can only be characterized as "primitives teaching primitives." Since teachers themselves have to be taught, the situation is observable even in the higher institutions of learning.[4] Similarly, universal political rights have thrown into the political arena hordes of dubious characters, to whom the state means little, the political game and its spoils everything. In varying degrees this pertains to most popular governments. De Tocqueville found it a pronounced feature of the United States already in the early nineteenth century. All this is part of the blurring of class distinctions, an undermining of "natural" stratification, a weakening of the evolutionary principle of complementarity. It is pregnant with the seeds of a new revolution or, this failing, of stagnation and decline. In this regard there is today not the least difference between the capitalistic-democratic and the communistic nations. Everywhere the doctrine of the equality of all has led to little else than the right of sterile minds to pose as leaders, especially in politics. It must be admitted, though, that it is extremely difficult to be a true leader in a domain where scientific truths and standards are not recognized and where, therefore, the reigning spirit is that of political alchemy or magic.

There is this saving factor in our present stratification, that at least in politics and public service power is not legally heritable. Our stratification is more fluid from generation to generation than at any other historical age. However, where it leads no further than a new class of sterile bosses every few years, it is in effect not too different from hereditary stratification. Fluid stratification, then, must by all means be preserved and furthered. It is one of the unquestionable gains brought about by the concept of freedom and equality. The positive achievements of modern Western civilization, as measured against medieval feudalism—in the arts, the sciences and scholarship—derive largely from the recognition of the fact that man does not breed true, that the great sons of obscure parents at all times outnumber the eminent sons of eminent fathers (be it for no other reason than that the obscure are thousands of times more numerous than the eminent). This is the rock on which the might of the Roman Church was built. A peasant boy can become Pope (the rest of its foundation is largely fiction).

Feudalism had nothing at all for its support but the fable of self-perpetuating nobility and grandeur. In the long run this aspect of human genetics might prove the deciding factor in the struggle between communism and capitalism. We could therefore hardly do better than aim at the restoration of the original division between civilization's *actual* creative elements and the guardians of tradition, which of course would be new in every generation, not hereditary. In a world in which political pugilism has reached bankruptcy, where development depends more and more on scientific insight and ideas, leadership will in the future no doubt fall to those most successfully drawing the practical consequences from these biological truths, those who are aware that the sociopolitical domain is the new frontier on which natural evolution now tries to deploy its forces.

Ideal systems will no doubt always remain "ideals." Human failings will always plague us. Still, the fact that there has never as yet existed a permanent civilization surely removes the need of delving to the bottom of the nature of political organization beyond idle speculation. Moreover, there is this highly important consideration: in a political system in harmony with natural evolutionary principles the mistakes of an individual leader would be minimized, while our present system can magnify them to tragic proportions. To illustrate this, we have but to think of the cost to generations following after us of Roosevelt's and Churchill's selling out the victory over Hitler to Stalin.

THE ABSOLUTE MALE

We saw that civilization began with the dominance of a small group of "new males" over a mass of representatives of an older way of life. The point to be emphasized here is that their abso-

lutism was *a psychological inevitability*. The necessity of it, however, did not arise, as might be thought, from the fact that the
grandiose schemes, born virtually with the first civilizations, depended for their realization on a mass of slaves; the real reason is
that civilization was initiated with the discovery of the new
mental habitat of rationality. And *rational thought is an absolute
mode of thought*. There never was anything absolute in the essentially ethical order of piety or the magic tenor typical of primitive
societies. On the other hand, absolutism in one form or another
has been the hallmark of all civilizations. Changes in the systems
of political management have never been anything but the sup-
planting of one form of absolutism by another—from monarchic
tyranny to the tyranny of the popular majority, in extreme form,
for instance, found in ancient Athens.

Apart from the purely political sphere, rational absolutism has
put its imprint on virtually every other domain of civilization. It
is reflected in the revolutionary concept of a single, absolute God,
first proclaimed by the Emperor Ikhnaton and possibly exported
from Egypt by the Hebrews, the absolutism of "god-given"
ecclesiastical and secular orders, the absolute value of religious
creeds and theological dogmas. Above all, it has inspired the belief
in the absolute superiority of the male over the female in all
spheres of life, from the family to the paternalism of kings and the
faith in the absolute dominance of commercial notions over everything else. And finally, though only in our own civilization, it has
engendered the belief in absolute determinism in the scheme of
nature and the illusion of an "exact" science. Only very recently
has science begun to move away from its initial absolutism, first
because of Einstein's Relativity, then because of Heisenberg's
Indeterminacy Relation.

The birth of male civilization and the birth of male absolutism,
then, were coeval and identical. Now, the notion of absolutes
always carries overtones of "the only right notion," "the only true
faith," "the only legitimate power," etc. Such concepts have often
imposed developmental restrictions as severe as those of primitive

rigidity or even, since civilization is more dynamic, actual malfunction. It always shows itself as the inability or unwillingness of the dominant stratum to recognize that stratification means complementary interdependence and that, therefore, spontaneous developments in one part of the social organism (even a lower stratum) call for adaptive modifications in the other divisions (even the supposedly absolute and eternally guaranteed ruling powers).

This is familiar, for instance, from the history of feudalism. But present-day democracies suffer from similar shortcomings. Economic absolutism is as sacred today as once were crowns and pedigrees. Under the modern corporate system the very concept of ownership has become as illusory as was the common participation in politics of king and people in the Middle Ages.[5]

This is not to say that the change from a landed to a monetary system of values was in itself deplorable. Taken within the entire developmental context, it does entail an enormous advantage, above all greater economic mobility and hence a reduction of the number and the severity of evolutionary obstacles. However, the crucial question here, too, is, to what extent can monetary absolutism remain evolutionarily creative? Compared with the tremendously accelerated development in science, it is beginning to look more and more like an atavism, one, at that, to which finance and management, as well as labor, are sworn.

The results of absolutism reveal themselves as particularly disastrous when political power becomes the hereditary property of a class representing an evolutionary stage which in other divisions of the body politic has already been superseded by newer developments, a more advanced mode of thought. The body politic is in such cases—for a change to avail ourselves of a biological analogy —like a human species with a cerebral cortex already capable of effective thought but all of whose actions are nevertheless still dictated by the older, instinctual midbrain. Such a species obviously would be cursed with a sort of generic schizophrenia.

A kind of "social schizophrenia" is, indeed, not unknown in

human history. Again, feudal dominance is the example closest at hand. For most of its life span it ruled over a world dominated (at least in Europe) by commerce, finance and industry, a world it could not understand, which it looked down upon—perhaps not unlike a reptile, proud of its seniority (if it has any thought), looking up contemptuously at the forked stick coming across its path, that upstart called man.

But the more tragic cases are presented by the still older forms of absolutism, evolutionarily still "older" brains, the hieratic ones. Sacerdotal rulers were always in a very real sense "incomplete men" because they remained untouched by developments considered essential to the more advanced masculine orders of life. Hence, every country, every early civilization in which priests achieved and maintained absolute rule succumbed to the blight of stagnation or became extinct. To no small degree, the early arrestment of Egypt was the result of a sacerdotal straitjacket. In time, the priests became, as in the case of our own medieval church, the most powerful body of vested interests, rulers absolute, a horrid flock of vultures living for two thousand years on the desiccating carcass of the land that had been the marvel of the world. The early stagnation of China under the tutelage of the secular priesthoods of Taoist and Confucianist sages with their unimaginative preoccupation with ritual and ceremony bears at least a resemblance to the case of Egypt. The Temple State of Judah perished because of the virtually pathological inflexibility, the absolutism of the notions of part of the sacerdotal caste. Similar factors occasioned the decline of the Aztec civilization of pre-Spanish Mexico and the realm of Mohammedanism, irrespective of whether there was an actual ecclesiastical ruling caste or only an almighty religious law attempting to fix human life for all eternity in a mold of steel.

All these represent cases of the absolutism of atavistic concepts, of "final answers" and "eternal verities" outliving their evolutionary usefulness, of "old brains" thwarting the budding new or trying to resorb it. Resorting here to Freudian terminology, one would even be justified in calling arrestment in priestly dominance a new form of the incestuous sin of Oedipus, celebrating its revival on the civilization level and in sacred camouflage producing tragedy after tragedy. For good reasons historians have associated the absence of an official priesthood in ancient Greece with the fact that it was there that the ideal of freedom first became a revolutionary social force.

All these manifestations of civilizations which have here been mentioned are generically male phenomena, upshots of the discovery by the first "new males," the founders of civilization, of the new mental habitat of strict rational thought. Absolute rational thought, as we now realize, is, however, not quite in agreement with fundamental natural law, since primal complementarity precludes all absolutism. One could justifiably thus sum up the history of all civilizations: faulty logic is worse than no logic.

"The problem of the male," as William M. Wheeler used to say, is founded in his absolute electric negativism, his essentially asocial nature, the restlessness and pugnacity of everything that is male. The phenomenal casualties among historic civilizations would seem to indicate that till now the negative aspects of the situation have always outweighed the positive. Wherever in history the "new male" or "complete male," representing the highest evolutionary stage of the moment, has attained unchecked dominance, he gave rise to little more than horrors: the barbarities of slavery, mass-slaughter, piracy, predatory nomadism, war and destruction for their own sake, the systematic plundering of the soil on which life depends, and even predatory respectability, as in purely commercial civilizations. Western dynamic genius in particular has always in the first place served extortionate ends, subjugation and exploitation within and without the West. Time and again it has pressed toward self-destruction: under a Church in armor, under feudal dominance, and under all bourgeois regimes. And even the temper of a large part of organized labor indicates that, if it could have things all its own way, it would conservatively drive time-honored predatory practices to the limit.[6]

These are only a few of the symptoms of the rule of the absolute male. They fill the major part of the book of history, to read which, with an open mind, is to become convinced that the male, left to himself and his dynamic negativism, is free only to destroy himself. As little as from the stagnant feminine pole is any enduring evolutionary freedom to be looked for from the dynamic-masculine.

What, then, of the role of woman in civilization?

CIVILIZED WOMAN

As was indicated, the original and decisive dichotomy, the mental speciation which is identical with the genesis of civilizations, left the entire maternal sex on the primitive side of the division together with the vast majority of primitive male subjects. This is true even of the women of the ruling class, though the social status and the amenities they enjoyed as wives, harem inmates, mothers, and daughters of the rulers tend to hide this fact. But even they contributed absolutely nothing to early civilizations. They had no active share in the numerous innovations distinguishing civilization from primitivity. Neither in the sphere of religion nor that of politics, neither in the engineering and architectural feats of early, and not so early, civilizations, nor in prescientific, philosophical and legal developments, nor in the field of the arts did they make the least contribution. The role of women, including that of the dominant stratum, remained essentially biological. Even at the time of the Great Cleopatra the essentially biological status of the queen was still symbolically manifest in that at public functions she appeared naked above the waist. By and large, indeed, the situation remained unchanged through millennia.

Only very recently in our own civilization has a revolution taken place. In part at least the factors behind this transformation are the same which permitted a large part of the once primitive mass of subject males to improve their social status. No doubt, new genetic complexes appeared also among the women, which gradually eroded or minimized the absolute dividing line between the rational and the biological sex, bringing about a partial assimilation of the heretofore primitive female to that of the "new," civilized male. A related phenomenon is often observed in animal evolution, where originally strictly male characteristics, such as horns, wings, or gorgeous coloring are ultimately transmitted to the females through genetic changes. Yet, as regards the human world, the obvious fact remains that, despite this rapprochement of the sexes, the creative contributions of the women, in our civilization as in all former ones, have remained almost negligible.

We touch here on a delicate subject, one, in fact, which has almost become taboo. The rigid hiatus between feminine domesticity and male public affairs, as it prevailed in Athens and through most of Western history, is of course no longer tenable in the modern world. There are countless kinds of work which can be done as well or even better by women as by men. The mingling of the sexes during the working day often has had a beneficial influence on both. I may be permitted here to refer to an unforgettable experience of my own early university years: the privilege, after having sat on school benches for years with nothing but boys, now to listen to lectures, sit in seminars and discuss a great variety of problems with young ladies. Most of my schoolmates had gone to the Institute of Technology, where women students were a rarity or lacking in those days. I actually pitied these boys. They would remain barbarians, I thought, whereas I was getting an education. My views have broadened since. Technologists for the most part are not barbarians, nor have I found all women "uplifting" or even a good public influence. Many have sacrificed a good part of their better nature in the competition with men.

The trouble is that the "double standard" cannot be fully eliminated without undoing nature. It is as out of the question as turning a plant into an animal. Today women are in politics and in the civil service, they hold academic and diplomatic posts. In all the middle-of-the-road routines, from factory, laboratory and

clerical work to shopkeeping, teaching, average to better scholarship and scientific research, in business and public administration,
novel-writing and medical practice, they employ techniques developed by men and trade in masculine products and ideas. To
this extent they have become part of masculine civilization. But
as soon as we move from the domain of routines to the creative
front ranks of civilization, we find the maternal sex prominent by
its complete absence. There is nowhere to be found a feminine
counterpart of Socrates, Christ, Michelangelo, Newton, Darwin
or Einstein. We have performing (i.e., routine) women artists as
brilliant as any of their masculine colleagues, but if they perform
great works, these are by men named Shakespeare, Bach, Mozart.
In all the visionary vanguards of civilization the difference between the winged male and the flightless female has basically remained the same as that among some moths and aphids. There
are indeed many women (Eleanor Roosevelt was among them)
who admit that this difference can never be expunged.[7] By and
large, then, the women have merely swelled civilization's "maintenance crew."

One might sum up the situation this way: as a civilized being,
woman shows signs of failing as man's complement. As such she
has hardly advanced beyond the biological, or at best the familial
level. In the sphere of civilization proper she is more and more
becoming man's echo. There is, though, danger in this situation.
For if complementarity is the evolutionary principle par excellence,
its annulment on any level can only mean the end of an evolutionary process.

It is typical of all traditionalists that they picture the future in
terms of the immediate past. This seems especially true of women.
The future hardly means more to most of them than, in the words
of René Dubos, "more of the same"—in our special case, still
greater equalization between the two halves of the species. In other
words, they have as a matter of principle accepted the basic absolutism of male dominance and leadership as final. A "better world"

to them seems one in which they are still more like men. They thus fail to provide, and hardly think of providing, the badly needed counterbalance to check the going-off-at-a-tangent of one-sided androcracy. If we look at the situation not merely from the viewpoint of the immediate past and the present, the insufficiency of this attitude becomes apparent. Evolution has never resulted from one sex's stepping into the worn-in shoes of the other sex. On the contrary, continuous differentiation has been its essence. Beyond any doubt, both sexes are equally important, and their importance lies precisely in their being different. Hence, the evolutionary value of their complementary nature can only increase, the further it is extended beyond bed and board.

However, we must not forget that all complementarity is possible only on a common ground. Differentiation can therefore never be absolute, as it tended to become under the old radical "double standard." For this reason, the recent rapprochement between the sexes and the reception of women in all departments of masculine civilization must by all means be welcomed. But—and this is an important *but*—it cannot be an end in itself. Within the larger evolutionary perspective we may liken it to the earlier integration of the males into the matronal families, their "rescue" from their somewhat meteoric asocial condition. No doubt this was an absolute necessity before the men could become evolutionary agents and bring forth civilization. The crucial point here is that their integration into the maternal families was not an end in itself. Where it was, where the males were satisfied with being good family fathers, no civilizations arose, or they remained arrested on a level not far from primitivity; similarly, with the assimilation of the women into civilization and potential future developments.

I think we should begin to realize that civilization is not necessarily now resting in a final masculine mold. Through aeons of time, evolution has slowly spiraled up through alternating relatively static and relatively dynamic phases, from the inanimate to the vital plane, from the vegetable to the animal kingdom, from matronal primitivity to patriarchal civilization. All this agrees too well with the fundamental order of the world—the imperceptible oscillation of emphasis between the spatial and the temporal side of the basic complementarity—to be accidental. We have reason, then, to expect the next potential evolutionary phase again to conform to a relatively static-vegetative-female mode. This would mean a new ascent of woman, or of a new kind of woman, as civilized, political man was a new kind of man. The world is waiting for "the new woman" to keep human destiny from a catastrophic ending in excessive masculinity. Evidently, this "new woman" cannot be an imitation man.

There will no doubt be difficulties, as there are in the way of all progress. Foremost among these is perhaps the fact that the maternal functions of woman cannot be eliminated, though it is exactly these which tend to keep her confined to a very narrow biological and social horizon. Yet one may at least imagine that precisely from maternal love may someday arise that new and larger ethos capable of overcoming the excesses of absolute, self-defeating and asocial rationality of which all civilizations have suffered or perished.

To conclude this chapter: the manifestations of political civilizations, like those of every phase of life, are not wholly accidental. Even the routine of their demise has been determined by natural factors, or, more precisely, their deviation from the most basic principle. None has expired, as Spengler would have it, because it completed a pseudo-biological cycle of birth, youth, maturity, old age and death. Civilization is *species integration* on the highest mental level, wherefore its laws cannot be those of the individual organism, but only those governing the life of the species.

Now, every species alive today has in fact existed from the beginning of life (though not usually in its present form) and can potentially continue to exist as long as life is possible on earth (not necessarily in its present shape). So that, if we gradually gain greater understanding of the laws of life as they relate to species, there is no reason why a civilization should not endure as long as the species. A prime condition for an enduring species-civilization obviously is that we stop deluding ourselves with the notion that sociopolitical man lives in one of the universe's vacuums, untouched by the laws of nature.

13

COSMIC LAW, HUMAN LAW AND FREEDOM

M AN does not live in a cosmic vacuum. In his basest as in his highest articulations he is a child of nature, with an inheritance he has gradually learned to trace back to the subatomic stratum.

Since Paracelsus (1493–1541) we have recognized that man's physique is not magically ruled by "four humors" but is an organism like that of every other animal. Galileo (1564–1642) mathematically demonstrated that even the size of man's body is in part, at least, determined by the law of gravity. A century ago Darwin convinced the world that man was not created as he now is but has become what he is through a process of evolution as long as life is old and that he may conceivably change still further. Thus Homo sapiens became accessible to scientific study.

For a long time, though, such studies remained confined mainly to man as an individual organism; there was occasion only for sporadic questions regarding the nature of human communities. Thus, that remarkable prophet of an evolutionary *Weltanschauung*, Johann Gottfried Herder (1744–1803), already stated clearly that "The entire human history is pure natural history," and again, "The God for whom I search in history must be the same he is in nature."[1] His compatriot Hegel (1770–1831) likewise sought for laws determining the course of history and of civilizations.[2] But probably the first who systematically studied human society as an extension of organic life was Auguste Comte[3] (1798–1857). However, his vision of the future state as "The Great Being," with a personal existence analogous to that of the individual organism, became the germ of an epidemic of intellectual confusion which has plagued even our century. Obviously, it is as senseless to consider the state a superior sort of animal as it would be to declare the animal a superior sort of molecule.

SOCIETY: A COSMIC MIRROR

Complementarity, in its dimorphic as well as its polymorphic forms, determines every sociopolitical system. The more faithfully the system mirrors the primal organizational and functional principle, the more it is healthy and natural. This sounds simple enough. In the organic world most living species have reached something close to perfection. In sociopolitical evolution, on the other hand, things have become bewilderingly complex, for the reason, obviously, that man must consciously create his systems and that creative thought, or at least the translation of thought into reality, is seldom spontaneous and usually hampered by mutually interfering tendencies.

In this chapter I wish to illuminate some other manifestations of complementarity and to show how far-reaching are its sociopolitical ramifications. In the purely social domain we have (some of them mentioned before) such pairs as employer and employee, landlord and tenant, producer and consumer, buyer and seller, student and teacher. In every case, both are necessary, both must benefit if a social event is to take place, and neither can become absolute without risking his own undoing. Then there are the many forms of multiple complementarity apparent in the almost infinite social division of labor, physical and mental. Here again, every individual field is only an aspect of a unitary whole; none is possible without the others. If one labor union strikes, a whole factory or industry is put out of gear. And in the case of a vital industry the business of a whole nation suffers. If the strike succeeds, the industry concerned must, or pretends to be forced to, raise its prices; dependent or related industries then also must, or pretend to be forced to, follow suit. Rising prices induce more strikes, and the chain reactions continue. Politicians, insofar as they think at all, find themselves faced with the problems: to what extent is collective bargaining (a legally sanctioned form of operative complementarity) an expression of social freedom, and to what extent blackmail? Or to what degree are price hikes an economic necessity, and to what degree extortion? Generally they do nothing about it for fear of being voted out of office and also because they have seldom grappled with the philosophical problem of the complementarity of law and freedom.

On the political plane, to which this example has brought us, we have as a further manifestation of complementarity the fact of the oneness of the biological species Homo sapiens and its subdivision into a variety of mental species. Politically this comes to a head in the delicate problem, never yet completely solved, of how to reconcile the doctrine of the equality of all with their factual inequality.

The bipartisan system of political representation poses related questions. Even in its most ingenuous form—the division into liberals (or progressives) and conservatives—it is full of mental pitfalls. Actually it should reflect the complementarity of the creative elements in a population and civilization's "maintenance crew"; but it never does because politicians themselves, with few exceptions, are part of the maintenance crew. The fact that each party is multiminded, with the shadings on both sides overlapping, usually makes a tolerable working scheme possible; still it is obvious that the system (even one of multipartisan representation) always leaves many citizens without any representation. The problem of how adequately to articulate a multiminded nation through a bipartisan system (i.e., polymorphic through dimorphic complementarity) is as difficult as that a choreographer would face were he to try to train a man-sized centipede to perform a solo dance in two-legged trousers.

We find a reflection of multiple complementarity in the political world in the familiar governmental divisions of legislative, executive and judiciary branches.

All these, and many more which could be mentioned, are still fairly extraneous manifestations of primal complementarity. How really far-reaching its implications are will best become apparent if we now turn to some of the more abstract, mental, sides of the sociopolitical sphere.

Foremost of all these problems is that of the complementarity of *law and freedom*. Nothing could illustrate better how intimately even the highest spheres of evolution merely reflect basic principles than the fact that the problem of law and freedom has become as important in modern theoretical physics as it has always been in politics. Where there is no freedom, law becomes superfluous nonsense, and where there is no law there is nothing at all, not even freedom. As aspects of one thing they stand and fall together. The practical side of this is, of course, that there can be no absolute law and no absolute freedom. Absolutism is an abomination to nature.

The application of this to political life and institutions is obvious. Insofar as political motives, on the part of groups of citizens or members of the government, are inspired by selfish instincts, they are absolutist because instinct is absolute, or near-absolute. This is precisely what so often makes political life the apotheosis of asocial behavior, even though it likes to pose under the halo of patriotism.[4] As in the beginning of civilization, it is still the expression of rationalized selfish animal drives and remains largely untouched by the more fundamental, salient feature of the new evolution—the ethical regulation of social functions, i.e., the sublimation of the primary social instinct.

But to continue with the more abstract manifestations of complementarity in the political sphere: here too the domain of the law supplies the outstanding examples. Since it is strictly man-made, far above the purely organic level, throughout human history it is often a plethora of aberrations. Yet, at its best, where

instinctual prompting has subsided, it usually reflects the Great
Law, complementarity. In our own political system the *due process
of law* is nothing else but complementarity in action, whereas
dictatorial absolutism, as a unilateral process, is its negation.[5]

In modern legal theory we recognize dimorphic complementarity
in the conceptual pair of *justice* and *legal security*. To many, they
may appear to be the same thing, as they no doubt were in primitive circumstances. Legal security, however, is tied to rigid formalism. Justice, on the other hand, is of the spirit, an impalpable,
evasive thing, the ever-present need, yet never within the reach
of the strict letter of the law and never really attainable in a life
ever changing. Every disregard of the complementary nature of
justice and legal security proves detrimental because no component
of the pair has any meaning by itself alone. Where legal security
is the only consideration, the law becomes stifling and thwarts
justice. On the other hand, all attempts to override the formal
law in the name of justice must needs annul security, i.e., the
foundations of the state, and therefore justice itself. In both absolute extremes the means destroys the end. "The possibility of a
maximum of *justice* must be paid for with a minimum of *security*,"
and "the extreme of *security* destroys *justice*." The quotation is
from a modern legal treatise,[6] but except for the words "justice"
and "security" it might well have come from a work on modern
basic physics.

Or consider another, closely related, pair: the *legal order* and
the *ethical order*. Originally they were one thing, and they still
are in the minds of certain primitives among us who always try
to raise their peculiar ethic to the status of the law of the land.
But one of the great formative principles of all evolution is that
of self-differentiation, the progressive complication of originally
simple units. By the same process the legal order and the ethical
order have differentiated out of the matrix of primitive custom.

Absolute reliance on people's ethic would quickly undermine
the legal order. Bona fide principles alone can never support the
state, nor can Kant's categorical imperative ever be a substitute

for the legal imperative. But neither can an advanced legal order persist without a complementary ethical order. Legal absolutism, as many historical examples prove, destroys man's conscience, because it declares conscience superfluous. But where individual ethic is dead, not even the formal law can survive: corruption rules supreme and moral dry rot corrodes society. On the other hand, there were cases of religious groups which emphasized the freedom and supremacy of the individual conscience, the "inner voice." Such ventures, too, usually ended in bankruptcy, be it because of the centrifugal tendencies of equally charged "free" consciences, or because they succumbed to the absolutism of a single individual whose "inner voice" bade him shout down the others.

The complete domain can be comprised only within the pair of law *and* conscience, or law and equity. This was known even to Aristotle. Christ, too, opposing the rigid rabbinical legalism of his day, expressed the same thought in the words, "the Law *and* the Prophets."

The same situation faces us in *justice* and *social security*. Within limits justice demands "social" security. On the one hand, however, absolute social security would be the social death sentence, the greatest injustice and demoralizing force. On the other hand, absolute justice could mean nothing but the meting out of "social" security according to people's deserts, which probably would entail insecurity for a greater number than is desirable for the security of the social whole.

As a last pair take *freedom* and *equality*, the chief tenets of the democracies. Only in self-delusion could one take them to be absolute separable realities. There never was in the world as little freedom and as little equality as when the French Revolutionists made deities of both of them. Nevertheless, they are realities in any community worth living in. But only complementary realities! Absolute freedom destroys equality because it comprises the right of the strong to enslave the weak (as at the beginning of the industrial order). Absolute equality destroys freedom because it is tantamount to spiritual death, creative entropy. We properly call "dead" all narrow religious groups or hidebound little democratic communities in which every individual idea is frowned upon as unorthodox, as a mark of conceit and overbearing. In the words of the jurist Schindler,[7] freedom absolute in the social world is the negation of responsibility, without which no state can exist, equality absolute the negation of vital organization. Freedom and equality, too, then, are yoked into a complementarity for which, if it could be couched in mathematical terms, Heisenberg's Uncertainty Relation would be the fitting formula.

EVOLUTIONARY FREEDOM

Since freedom, as a concomitant of complementarity, is a very relative thing and since, as we pointed out in Chapter 5, early man can have had very little of it, it is worth casting a quick glance at the factors operative in its development. Though these observations will be in the nature of a slight diversion, they will deepen our insight into the close connection between complementarity and freedom.

Among the characteristics which set off man from the other animals is his relationship to the future. Animals have it too, of course, though with them the future remains part of the instinct complex. With man, on the other hand, it has become an important part of his conscious orientation. Since animals have memories, we may assume that, insofar as they at all deal consciously with the time dimension, such consciousness is mainly directed to the present and the past. The first true human being, accordingly, was one who knowingly looked into the face of the future. Even today, whether we conceive life as a constant sinking into the past or a continuous emergence into the future, determines a significant side of our nature. Our lives are shifting knots in the complementarity of past and future. Undoubtedly, the beginnings of the concept of the future were extremely modest. They may have been no more than the hope of finding a flint better suited to a certain purpose, or the hope of a better cave. And it is virtually certain that such hopeful dealings with the world were wholly restricted to nonhuman objects, whereas the relations of man to man continued for a long time to be subject to instincts. The body social was as little amenable to purposeful modification as the individual physique. It is so even today. It is easier to travel to the moon than to overcome the ingrained traditions ruling the social world.

At what stage of development early man first became aware that his social bodies also were involved with the future is of course impossible to say. It is, however, a very important aspect of the conversion of animals into human beings. One is justified in assuming that this increasing awareness of a "social future" was part of the process of the converting of instincts into ethical behavior or, as we put it before, of "complementarity rising to consciousness," however inchoate at first. Most certainly, men had no words to express all this, nor that concomitant of complementary interdependence we now call freedom. Probably even among the most intelligent all this remained but hazy notions. The gist of it, then, is (1) that what human freedom there is, in the last analysis, arose from the growing awareness of the complementarity of past and future; (2) that freedom began as an extrasocial manifestation and only much later was perceived as a social potentiality. To the extrasocial manifestations or the extrasocial orientation belonged the religious beliefs; these offer the most definite signs of a preoccupation with the future and the increasing importance freedom assumed in the vision of the future. To make this clear one need but refer to the Messianic hopes of the Jews, which were at least hopes of a future free from foreign yokes, whereas "internal" social freedom hardly entered into the picture.

It must be reckoned one of the greatest evolutionary advances when bodies of men began to think independently enough of religious traditions to perceive freedom as an internal social concern, something in their own keeping and no longer in the hands of the gods. Some of the Greeks, especially the Athenians, were the first to reach this stage. Insofar as the concept of freedom became embodied in the Christian tradition, it is largely part of our Greek heritage. For the other part, however, it must be regarded as an intrinsic aspect of every incipient civilization, at least of the ruling "political species." For within their own stratum the dominant caste often evinced a degree of freedom which one is tempted to call "class democracy," within which the king was only *primus inter pares*, the first among equals. One may say, then, that a significant measure of freedom entered human life only with civilizations and that it was from the beginning innately allied to willed development. This agrees well with what we said in the beginning: that the freedom of life is essentially the freedom of evolution, i.e., the result of the continuous elaboration of the theme of complementarity.

From what has been said so far, other facts and prospects can be derived. It merits repeating that individual freedom precedes social freedom. This is not surprising, since the degree of freedom a man attains depends on the development of his brain. Most people still think of freedom as an individual prerogative. Yet individual and social freedom go hand in hand, for the obvious reason that every evolutionary change begins with individuals and then is propagated in the population through the processes of reproduction. Furthermore, the complementarity of law and freedom, of which we spoke above, is operative even in evolution, where "law" stands for the determinism embodied in the countless mechanisms of organic systems. Because determinism remains so overwhelming, there are still many scientists who deny that there is any freedom in the world. (One wonders, though, how they would react to a law forbidding them to teach the illusoriness of freedom.) There is not the slightest doubt that we are mostly ruled by a deterministic scheme, from conception, through embryology, in the countless chemical and physical processes of the body and the mysterious working of our brains. Certainly the vast majority of unconscious goings-on in our systems obey the laws of mechanistic determinism. However, it would seem to follow from the complementarity of past and future, at the node of which our lives are spent, that strict law is essentially connected with the past, whereas the future can never be fully determined. Only the past is fully determined. Determinacy thus reveals itself essentially as evolutionary and ontological routine, the dictate of precedents in the history of the species and of the individual. And as the manifestation of routine it is almost bound to break down occasionally in face of novel situations. It is only at such moments, too, that full consciousness comes into play and where, therefore, we get a chance to make free decisions.

But there is another side to this problem. Our personal freedom within the order of nature may be minute, much less than we like to think. On the other hand, since evolution operates through the species, the potential freedom mankind may yet fall heir to may wax all the more. Here again, complementarity seems to be the supreme law: the greater the freedom the individual claims for himself, the smaller must be the share of the species (or the body politic), and hence the evolutionary potential. But it is likewise implicit in the involved mystery of complementarity that if there were no individual freedom, if man were a mere automaton, the evolutionary chances of the species would also be nil.

In a way, man has of course always known or sensed this. For whenever individuals or groups have tried to make *certain* they had things all their own way, when they assumed absolute powers, they could do so only at the cost of others' freedom, or of the freedom of the society to which they belonged. But freedom and strict certainty, or absolutism, are mutually exclusive. Every attempt to reduce the uncertainties intrinsic in life to a strictly calculable scheme, an absolute law, results in a loss of freedom and a degeneration of life. The countless potentialities of life then are replaced by the one certainty of a slow death. Strict certainty and absolutism of any kind—political, economic, scientific or theological—has always shut the door on evolution, which is the essence of life's freedom. And written history is hardly more than the record of continuous attempts to thwart freedom by one scheme of absolutism or another.

As is well known, the fantastic rise of physical science and of technology since the beginning of the nineteenth century has been accompanied by a parallel movement to mechanize life itself. The ideal of totalitarians and collectivists of all hues has been, and still is, the perfectly determined push-button mechanism, an engineered national economy, an architectured national conscience, a factory-made national behavior, an automatic moral, a standardized superarmy of factory-trained mechanics supervising the working of the monster robot—in short, the substitution of death for life, of absolute certainty for the uncertainties of freedom. For ages, of course, some people have been willing to barter away life's freedom for the dubious certainty of post mortem social security. But the danger is spreading. Even the democracies are succumbing to the fatal trend. Big Business and Big Labor have long been organized on the mechanistic totalitarian pattern. Today excessive bureaucracy is tending in the same direction.

But instead of pursuing this not very encouraging situation, we had better turn to its more fruitful "negative" side, which is uncertainty. We have seen again and again that complementarity means the integration of at least two disparate units into a whole of a superior order, a Gestalt so intricately balanced that none of the units can exist without the others.

The question now arises: what freedom, then, is left the human individual caught in the fantastic maze of complementarities making up the body politic?

INDIVIDUAL FREEDOM

Since Rousseau's day the outcry has been that society robs the individual of his freedom and reduces him to a mere cog in a monstrous machine. Well, does it?

If in the foregoing subchapter attention was drawn to the complementary relationship between the freedom of the individual and the evolutionary freedom of the species or its closest representative, the body politic, the intention was in no way to revive

Rousseau's doctrine. The relationship in question is more complex than Rousseau could imagine. In the simplest terms it works out as follows: though evolutionary freedom is primarily or exclusively a matter concerning the species, its results are bound to reflect back on its individual constituents—to be sure, those only of later generations—for they are the species.

In order to eliminate personal prejudices touching upon this problem, let us first approach it by way of a simple geometrical analogy and ask: what can you do with an isolated point-in-space representing the individual? You can make a mental note that it is there, that is all. But add a second point and you not merely have another point to incorporate in your mental inventory, you "get something in the bargain." Immediately there is a potential *relation* between the two points, which in the simplest case we express by connecting them with a straight line denoting distance. Distance is one of the unexpected emergents between two points.

Now add a third point. This time you get a number of "extras at no extra cost." First, the third point gives you two new distances. Second, it makes you expand from one dimension into two; in place of a line you have a plane. Third, the three distances enclose a further something that is new: an area. Fourth, each pair of distances or line intervals wraps up another unexpected bargain: an angle. So that, instead of merely three isolated points, there are now, in addition, three distances, three angles, an area and a plane.

Now add still another random point, and from a two-dimensional plane you barge forth into three-dimensional space, the world of solids or volumes. And, incidentally, by barging forth you have automatically added a fourth dimension, that of time. But with space and time, or space-time, we have almost the whole universe, certainly considerably more than the four isolated points would add up to.

A mere inventory, we see, misses the chief things. Anywhere outside the inventorist's mind and textbooks of arithmetic you get shortchanged and defrauded in the most outrageous manner by a faith in the sum total. Anthropomorphically and in a loose way, we may say that the four points of our geometric example, because they refused to remain four isolated points and made the best of their potential relations, became "free" to create among themselves something of a much higher order than four individual points— the whole science of geometry. Yet, as mere points they sacrificed nothing, as points they remained as good and perfect as solitary specimens.

Parabolically this gives us a preliminary answer to our question concerning the freedom of the individual within social systems. In a purely biological way, the human equivalent of an isolated point-in-space might be considered "free," but free merely from the greater freedom conferred by social relations. If his freedom were absolute, the species itself would evidently cease to exist, and hence the individual himself. The old dogma, that society is nothing but an atomized mass of individuals, which secular and ecclesiastical authoritarianism did its best to promote (because it alone could justify tyranny), is one of the most corrupt and devilish inventions ever foisted on mankind. Cultures and civilizations, like the science of geometry between related points, arise only where many individuals assume complementary roles within one all-embracing superior event. Where this condition is lacking, nothing at all can ever happen.

No isolated individual therefore has any "free and independent" existence save that of a wild animal, never that of a truly human being. Man can be human only in human society. It is today accepted as an unquestionable scientific fact that he could become Homo sapiens only in the stimulating atmosphere of a social environment, which, in our basic terms, means the most elaborate field of manifold complementarities. As was pointed out before, his very brain is a social brain, the gift of society; it could never have become what it is in zoological isolation. Whatever freedom man possesses he enjoys only because he is yoked into relationships with a great many others.

The freedom which is apparent in evolution and in all life has from the beginning been founded on the principle of complementarity. And because human social systems represent the extreme elaboration of this basic theme, man can potentially become the freest of all creatures. He can be *creatively* free. The hermit, the pious recluse, the "rugged individualist," for the most part are stupid frauds or vicious parasites. They have merely made off with their loot of cultural or monetary values, like thieves vanishing into the night to dissipate their booty. The true solitaries, if there were such, would by a law of nature be barred from all values, all fruits of culture and civilization, because they would be simple animal organisms.

Life began with a type of physical system that was unique in that it made itself dependent on the environment, made the environment its complementary partner. But such dependence had its compensations. The stronger and more manifold it was, the more of the potentialities of the environment were opened to the organism. In being no longer self-contained, the organism transcended itself; the more it did so, the more the links with the environment became conscious. Philosophically speaking, *the very nature of life is self-transcendence,* even on levels to which it is hard to attribute consciousness. This is what distinguishes organisms from inert systems. If it were otherwise, no life, and no social life, of course, could ever have arisen. Sociopolitical life, as man experiences it, is the highest form of life precisely because in its best aspects it is the apotheosis of self-transcendence. The same idea can be expressed biologically, sociologically, or in economic, ethical and religious language, but its essence is always the one same scientific truth. Only if one forsakes all scientific integrity, only if one denies all that has been recognized as scientific fact in the diverse fields of objective research on man, can he possibly come to any other conclusion. Because self-transcendence in its most conscious form, the way man knows it, is simply the recognition of a truth already stated: the truth of the unity of life and of the brotherhood of man. This wording, incidentally, just to show that the conclusions arrived at here are not singular, has been borrowed from an eminent evolutionist, George Gaylord Simpson.[8]

Whatever we treasure most in life, all its highest values—love, friendship, ethical conduct, the power of reason, the arts and sciences, religion—all these are emergents of the sociopolitical field and the self-transcendence of the individual which social life implies. Human societies and political civilizations can show results beyond the attainment of any single individual precisely because, instead of defying fundamental law, they fulfill it to an eminent degree. And they can achieve results only to the extent to which they are faithful to basic law. Self-transcendence thus becomes an important aspect of species integration on the mental level, i.e., of political organization.

It is species integration on the highest mental level which in man's world has brought forth the majesty of thought, of mental vision, visionariness and imagination. "Wolf-children," the exemplary "free and independent" individuals, who had only the upbringing of solitary wild animals, have therefore a thinking power no greater than that of apes. They missed the critical time at which society makes accessible her greatest treasure, thought, and they never catch up again. No man in his right mind would call them free. No "rugged individualist" would change places with them because he would have to sacrifice the power of thought, which he owes to society and often uses to no better purpose than to prey on society.

Everything that is truly human in man, and not merely animal, is the gift of society, from the faculty of spoken language to what human freedom there is. Here are emergents of the process of species integration on the highest level of evolution, resulting from the freeing of energies through cooperation, integrated functional specialization. It is this process which frees many individuals from lowly tasks and allows them to specialize in seeing and thinking. But their ideas themselves in time become integrated into fields of thought, social traditions, those peculiar ethnic "ways of seeing things" which lend a unique note to the customs, arts, religions and philosophies of the various cultures.

All these manifestations of culture or civilization are in the truest sense social visions, expressions of a singular outlook common to large groups, to which artists and other creative minds have merely given the most succinct form. No human genius has ever arisen in a social vacuum. None of the arts, sciences or religions is at all imaginable as the emanation of "free and independent" individuals, or of a Coney Island crowd of "rugged individualists." They are possible only as the flowering of the play of energies become free through the integration of many into unitary social fields.

The normal individual member of a highly evolved society therefore has in no way become degraded to a meaningless cog within a monstrous machine. On the contrary, he has attained a freer life, a *dual* life, that of a specialist and that of a full-fledged personality. As one note does not make music and conveys no meaning, but only the context of the entire score gives character and content to each individual note, so also the human individual can develop character, personality, a sense of *Eigenwert*, as the Germans say, and of responsibility only in social integration. The individual depends as much on the social environment as the latter on individuals. They are complementary aspects of one single phenomenon.[9]

Of all animals, man is anatomically the least specialized, the most universal. His specialization is mental and social. The relational nature of all life has found its highest expression in human society, and this—thought being the recognition and formulation of relations—is precisely what makes him the only thinking being, the only ethical creature. Relatedness is everything. As the highest embodiment of this truth, man has been able to progress to the greatest degree of species integration, which is of the essence of the evolutionary trend in life. This is what has given him the power to direct his own evolution, but also to misdirect it if he derives his guiding principles from shortsighted, fractional, individual or group considerations, instead of from the evolutionary laws of the species. Therein lies his greatest freedom, as well as his greatest danger.

Because man is a constituent as well as a maker of society, he can be both specialist and universalist, like Spinoza earning his living in the narrow groove of a grinder of lenses while his mind explored the whole universe. Only to the extent to which he is both a specialist and a universalist is he a truly human being, and only the society which permits and encourages its members to be human beings of this kind can be a truly free society, that is, one which is free to grow, to continue to evolve.

14

INDIVIDUAL AND STATE

Einstein and other physicists have on many occasions made the seemingly paradoxical statement that the true enrichment of science consists in the impoverishment of its conceptual scheme, meaning that science is the more scientific the better it learns to subsume a multiplicity of phenomena under a few general concepts, or even a single one. In principle this would be the same development our early ancestors went through (and which some primitives still have before them). It began when it occurred to a prehistoric genius that all those things growing about him—oak, birch, maple, beech, spruce, pine, etc.—could be gathered under the one name of *tree*, and all those nonhuman creatures—wolf, bear, stag, lynx, fox, rabbit, etc.—could be called *animals*. This is the step from the specific to the general, from the concrete to the abstract.

The physical sciences have closely approached the ideal of one universal formula. The biological sciences, dealing with an infinitely more complex sphere, are still far from it but do recognize a handful of directive principles. The social sciences, however, struggling with the most involved tangle of related facts and fictions, seem hardly to have thought of the possibility of unifying concepts. Nonetheless, they do recognize society, whereas a century and a half ago Goethe could still say that he acknowledged only individuals and did not know what people were talking about when they spoke of society.

In this discussion we have persistently followed the view that the social systems of man must be regarded as the final phase of animal evolution, which from certain protozoa up represents a trend toward species integration. This permits the gathering of an important side of the seemingly fractured evolutionary picture under a single aspect. It obviates the need of treating man as a sort of brilliant outcast from the animal kingdom; quite the contrary, it incorporates human societies into that one body of well-established facts and theories known as science. As there is but one nature, there can be only one science; what does not fit into a unified world picture can hardly be scientific.

SPECIES INTEGRATION

The trend we designate as species integration is but the application of the complementarity principle to the life phase of evolution. It allows us to subsume both the physical and the biosocial sciences under one aspect, to regard all evolution as the elaboration of one basic and universal theme. Whether we deal with atoms, molecules, single-celled creatures, multicellular plants or animals, plant, animal or human societies, the fundamental organizational principle is always the same, always integration on the basis of complementarity, of from two to billions of diverse constituents into entities of a higher order.

Because species integration is the gist of life's evolution it also becomes the crux of political organization and hence one of the central problems of creative politics. The integration with which we are here concerned is never a repressive or compulsory principle; rather must it be called spontaneous and voluntary. It cannot be imposed on any system, as you cannot impose democracy on a flock of chickens or on a human strain not mature for it. Since politics in its highest aspects is one of the supreme manifestations of species integration, it is important that we come to a clear understanding of what it means.

Far from being confined to the human sphere, multi-individual species integration begins on the very lowest animal levels. A species is more than a mere theoretical collective of like specimens. It is itself an actual organism, though as yet a very loose organism indeed. It is something like an evolutionary guerrilla army, of which we rarely see more than one or a few members. Hence, with his pronounced and often warped individualism man has for millennia been incapable of grasping the larger and more fundamental reality of the invisible organization of the species. This became apparent for the first time through the genetic research of Sewall Wright and his school, who demonstrated that in most kinds the integrative process has advanced enough to make a considerable number of specimens a "must" for a species to be viable. A single pair is generally too small a fragment of the vital whole to guarantee survival. Noah's legendary assembly of one pair of each kind would have proved as useless to repopulate the earth after the flood as if he had collected just one individual of a kind. The species or, in practice, the local population is then the decisive reality. And though new gene complexes initiating evolutionary advances (or regressions) always arise in individuals, they can become effective only through the "gene pool" of a population, representing the basic integrative level. In Simpson's words, "it is populations, not individuals, that evolve."[1]

Before we consider some of the political aspects of species integration we must understand clearly that political integration is merely a continuation on the highest mental level of a trend that dominates all biological evolution. Wherever there is even a beginning of biological species integration, every individual bears in, or on, its body the anatomical symbols of this fact. Among these the sexual characteristics are outstanding. The organs of one reproductive half of a species are mere freaks without the complementary organs of the other half, and the same holds true for other parts of animal anatomy. In man, for instance, the organs of speech and the corresponding cortical areas make sense only as the correlates of the auditory apparatus of other individuals. Most of anatomy is, indeed, a record written in protoplasmic symbols of the individual's environmental relations. Where, therefore, as in the case of man, the species has become the dominant part of the environment, the anatomical correlates of species integration make up an astonishing part of individual anatomy. Take away these parts embodying species relations and you have—God knows what, but certainly no human being.

If the human brain, for example, may be read as the anatomical annals in which is recorded the largest part of the story of species integration, then, obviously, the manifestations of this brain, all conscious and many unconscious brain activities, are likewise the fruit of such integration. Even the greatest geniuses in the history of mankind are merely the blossoms and fruits of a process of biological and mental integration reaching back to the beginning of the species, or even further. The individual's attributes and achievements, therefore, are never his own exclusively, but to a far greater extent than we generally realize those of the species.

To give but one example: countless people unknown to the author have collaborated on this book, people stretching over millennia and over the globe. The "team work" began with the first philosophers and gradually included thousands of physicists, chemists, biologists, anatomists, physicians, religious leaders, historians, sociologists, jurists and political thinkers. To these must be added everybody who contributed his mite to the evolution of the language in which the book is written, those who invented and perfected the art of writing and printing, etc. In the last analysis, then, any author's part in a book is modest, his known and unknown collaborators did most of the work; the final process is essentially one of reintegrating into a new form data that have long been available, of seeing them in a new light.

Thus, mind, as the supreme exponent of the dynamic-animalic division of the human organism, became the chief social organizer and made Homo sapiens the only species on earth whose social bodies have discarded physiological organization.

Thought itself is, indeed, integrative power at its very highest in that it either discovers integral connections within the system of nature or employs the process of integration for creative purposes, as in the arts, in science and technology, and in the elaboration of social systems. Thought is the most precious bloom of the integral whole of the species, and it is as true that it was born of species integration as that it made further species integration possible. The two versions are but different aspects of one single process. And so extensive already is the process that today we must begin to give thought to the possibility of gathering all mankind in a single system.

So much for the individual's subordination to the species.

But as always in life, a vital situation has more than one aspect. The thinking brain may literally be a "social brain" and "the gift of society," but it always remains the brain of an individual. Society as a whole never thinks. And though thought is absolutely unimaginable save as an emergent of species integration, the process of thinking is nonetheless always delegated to individuals, particularized in individual brains. In principle we have here, then, exactly and identically the situation we met on the very lowest biological level, where genetic mutations always arise in the individual but can become effective evolutionary factors only through the gene pool of a population.

In other words, from the very lowest to the very highest evolutionary level individual and species (or population) remain complementary aspects of a single phenomenon. Hence the inescapable fact that, according to the viewpoint we occupy, the social whole —especially in the long view—becomes the only reality with which we can deal, whereas the individual shrinks into a shadowy, at any rate fleeting, existence. And on the other hand—in the short view —the individual is often virtually the only concrete phenomenon accessible while society is an abstraction. Both viewpoints are valid, even vital, but either by itself alone is irrelevant, unrealistic, indeed corrupt.

Politically that means, of course, that individual and state too fit into no other framework than that of complementarity. They too are merely aspects of a single phenomenon. The problem posed by the relationship of individual and state, as well as of groups and the state, represents merely the most involved of all variations on the fundamental cosmic theme. Nobody will deny its intricacy. So complex is it, indeed, that it took thousands of years of civilization before it was recognized as a problem. And since the ancient Greeks and Chinese, the first who wrestled with it, we have made little progress.

In the complementary relationship of individual and state—and groups and the state—we thus envisage the most formidable task man ever has encountered, and it will be with him as long as he lasts. Conquering outer space is a kindergarten pastime by comparison, if not actually an infantile escape, conscious or unconscious, from our more urgent problems; it is akin to the old political expedient of launching an aggressive war as a way out of harassing internal vexations. It is certain that, because the complementarity of individual and state is a matter of species integration, it cannot be expected to find even a halfway satisfactory solution save on a species-wide scope.

This is not a plea for an immediate consolidated world-state or for indiscriminate global promiscuity. Quite the contrary. Even dyed-in-the-wool internationalists should bear in mind that no evolution has ever taken place save on the basis of diversification and segregation. Not in the absolute sense of course, but in a complementary one: by keeping the products of self-differentiation separate and yet integrating them functionally into a higher unitary system, by delegating a certain autonomy to each individual constituent, organ and division. In the history of humankind the races, subraces, cultures, states, towns and villages represent such subsidiary units. Their autonomy has never been complete and especially under modern conditions is more and more becoming a figment of reactionary brains, just as at the other extreme the monolithic global species-state is a pipe dream of unrealistic Marxism and the very denial of evolution.

With equally profound distrust should we view the forecast of a certain school of biologists for a homogenized human dough to be achieved through the eventual merger of all races. The theory mentioned is a classical example of the cardinal scientific sin of drawing universal conclusions from limiting cases. It is based on the indubitable certainty that all human strains are genetically compatible, i.e., capable of producing fertile hybrid offspring. But it arbitrarily disregards the fact that above the lowest common denominator, the germ plasm, incompatibilities appear and mushroom. As everybody is aware by now, human blood has diversified into many incompatible types. Transfusion of the wrong blood amounts to manslaughter. On the still higher level of body tissue the individual already proves so unique as to reject grafts from another individual. And though medical technology has recently achieved a modicum of success in artificially conditioning foreign tissue for acceptance, such partial (and never enduring) success has been confined to tissues and organs of the relatively primitive vegetative system. On theoretical grounds at least transplants would seem to be well-nigh or altogether out of question on the higher stages of the neuromuscular and the central nervous systems.

This suggests that in the highest evolutionary spheres, that of the conscious mind, there may be more incompatibilities than we even dare suspect, which, if improperly handled, may become barriers to further evolution. The whole problem is of course an aspect of that of mental speciation; but we need not pursue it further here. Suffice it to repeat what we said when speaking of symmetry and asymmetry among molecules. All life, all evolution, depends on asymmetry, the integration of unequals, on potentials possible only where there are differences, whereas complete egalitarianism is the organizational form nearest to death. A homogenized humanity could hardly be more interesting than a sand pile and no doubt would be at the end of its evolutionary tether.

INDIVIDUALISM

We saw that individual and state are but complementary aspects of a single phenomenon. According to our definition of complementarity, this means that neither can have any absolute meaning and in practice may never become sovereign or absolute except to the irreparable harm of both. In order to understand the full import of this on political life we must take a closer look, first at the individual, then (in the next section) at the state.

A vast amount of law is concerned with the position of the individual within the body politic. It defines his duties and his rights (also a complementary pair) without really coming to grips with what the individual actually is. He is generally taken for granted, probably in the spirit of an ancient religious tradition considering him one of the ultimate realities.

Contrary to widespread opinion, the really revolutionary movement in human evolution is not collectivism, but the individualistic trend in history. Collectivism in all its forms is in the most literal sense reactionary, a throwback to primitivity, in which the group spirit was all, the individual nothing. On the other hand, wherever individual development has gone to extremes, we generally find the tables turned and men incapable of seeing the body politic for persons.

Like so many other aspects of sociopolitical evolution, the relationship of individual and state has a biological basis, and this we must explore first.

Every civilized human being is both a unique individual and a representative of the species. His species part is the germ plasm contained in the reproductive glands. The other part is the soma, that side of the organism which between conception and maturity undergoes a tremendous development and whose supreme manifestation is the mind. Now, there exists between animals and man a remarkable divergence, obvious in the simultaneous maturing of soma and sex cells in the first and a differential one in man. When the germ plasm is ripe, the animal's soma is ready for reproductive functions, whereas man's is not.

Our positive knowledge regarding the situation is limited. The Dutch anatomist Louis Bolk[2] discovered that at about the fourth year of life a schism takes place in human development. At this age the germ plasm of the child, especially of the girl, is virtually mature, but the soma far from fully developed. Even before Bolk, Freud had drawn attention to a psychological crisis attending this phase of infantile development, which he identifies with the birth of the ego. The human ego, in Freud's view, is merely a substitute for the objects of (subconscious) erotic desires awakening at this age, objects which remain of course unattainable because of somatic immaturity. This interpretation, like so much of Freud, is surprisingly one-sided. Even at the lowest animal levels there is, after all, considerably more to life than sex. Still, the problem we are here confronting no doubt is that of the birth of the ego. The latter is, however, more likely to be the result of certain exclusively human cerebral developments than of something which is part of the lowest common denominator of all animaldom. For the temporary arrestment of the sex cells before final maturation, which Bolk showed to hold for man, had long been known from the cytology of the lower animals. Man is extraordinary only with regard to the duration of this arrestment. And it cannot be questioned that this is what gives the brain a chance to become truly human. For with the beginning of this gonadic arrestment there is initiated an enormous extension of the axon-dendrite system, integrating countless hitherto unrelated and only now maturing cortical cells, thus making "the brain essentially the organ of personality." It is at this point that the most important complementarity in human life comes into play. The more the mental aspect of the child develops, the more the animal recedes. The brain, however, is the chief mediator between the organism and the world at large. For this reason a valid explanation of the birth of the ego can hardly be derived from any other basis than the original "life situation," i.e., the organism-environment complementarity. Such an explanation, incidentally, was already given by the philosopher Martin Buber.[3] In Buber's view, the birth of the ego is the result of a self-differentiation, literally the *"ec-stasis,"* the separation of the *I* from the primitive infantile selfsameness of the *I-Thou* or the *I-It.*

From this point on, according to Bolk, human development is

monopolized by the soma dominated by the newborn ego, whereas
the quasi-mature germ plasm remains arrested for years. This
polarization into an animalic species part and a self-conscious
individual part comes to a new crisis with puberty, when the soma
approaches the end of its development and the germ plasm
"catches up" again after having been repressed for a decade. The
animal knows no puberty in the same sense as man does. With
the human being it is the mind's tremulous awakening to the fact
that the organism of which it is the efflorescence is also an instrument of the species, an animal being. The tensions of puberty
represent the second major developmental crisis in man, the first
conscious crisis; it is usually more acute on higher than on lower
levels of individual development. The issue is now which of the
two poles shall dominate, the species part or the individual part,
the animal or man, instinct or mind. If the animal gains the upper
hand, development comes to an end. A nascent complementarity
of tremendous evolutionary value is rescinded. The more advanced
human strains and individuals, on the other hand, distinguish
themselves from the more backward ones precisely in that they
have learned permanently to maintain, to institutionalize, in their
organisms the creative germal-somatic polarity. They have succeeded in rendering productive that strange "harmony of opposites" between a bundle of animal instincts and thought.

We have every reason to recognize here one of the most important roots of sociopolitical evolution, its twin taproots, so to
speak. Out of the complementarity of soma and germ plasm develops that of individual and state.

The closer a human strain is to the animal world, the more
disastrous is puberty to social evolution. On the lowest human as
on the animal level, sexual maturity always means the clock's
stroke of twelve, after which the cycle of generation begins anew
without ever getting beyond the noon of puberty and the narrowest
family. Puberty on this level means an estrangement from individual knowledge and activity, a relapse into species knowledge
and species activities, exhausting themselves in the knowledge of

the other sex and the exploration of the instinct domains of nutrition and defense.

How different are the concomitants of puberty among the more advanced strains and individuals! The germ plasm, the lowest common denominator and binding element of the species, begins, as it were, to irradiate and under the guidance of the mind to transcend both individual and species, thus kindling a desire for knowledge far beyond instinctual objects. It is this personal striving alone which permits that extensive elaboration of the social fabric into what we have come to call civilization.

But there lies a treacherous pitfall along this road. A degree of individual development may finally be reached which is hard to distinguish from the intense self-consciousness of incipient puberty itself. The ego then seems so completely to absorb the species as to make it difficult to tell which dominates which. Instinct-ridden animality becomes transformed into a fulminant, passionate individualism, and the individual regards himself as autonomous, absolute to the point of becoming subversive. The effect on the social whole is no different from that of puberty itself on primitive levels; it is disruptive, atomizing.

We may therefore fittingly speak of a second, "social," puberty.

This constitutes one of the great dangers of all advanced societies. All those experiencing the fervor of individualistic extremism hover on the brink of ruin, of dissolution and dissoluteness, and the downfall of a number of civilizations began with this "social puberty," the disintegration inevitable with the complete liberation of the individual from social ties.

The late period of classical Greece and Rome at the height of the empire are the outstanding examples; the Italian Renaissance furnishes another. Life during those epochs teemed with round, vivid and full-spirited personalities, exhibitionists for the most part —fire-eaters, swashbucklers, self-advertisers, bombastic noise-makers and other dogs with more bark than pedigree, great pirates, robber barons, tyrants, renowned prostitutes, virtuosos in the art of murder and high treason—but also an exquisite minority of noble cast, great philosophers and poets, sculptors, painters, architects. All of them were exponents of extreme individualism, minds glorying in their uniqueness.

There is a school of thought which holds this state of things to be the absolute summit of human development—Nietzsche is its great prophet. Spengler, who is closely related to Nietzsche, would have it that after such great periods of individualism the downfall is inevitable, final. It would be imprudent to minimize the perils with which every such carnival of individualism is fraught. But to identify a period like the Italian Renaissance with the *non plus ultra* of human achievement would itself seem possible only within a "puberty philosophy." From a broader, scientific, outlook we must insist that, if in the evolution of the species a time arrived when puberty no longer proved a solvent to the family, there is no cogent reason why it should not be possible to prevent the orgies of individualism from exploding civilizations.

The advent of individualism, then, is a threshold phenomenon and a crisis akin to puberty. Both appear necessary as nature's tests to determine whether a biological strain is fit or not to proceed to a higher level. In both instances the only evolutionarily sound solution of a crisis lies in making permanent, in equilibrating, the complementarity of ego and species; for it is in the nature of things that the absolute Either as well as the absolute Or means annihilation of both.

The individual remains one of the essential conditions of social evolution. In every field of human endeavor, every single step forward was first taken by an individual, the rest then followed. This is a necessary consequence of the fact that the thinking brain is always an individual brain. But this in no way gives it carte blanche, for the simple reason that thought can be fruitful only within the framework of the body politic. Each leader is a leader only thanks to his following. And since absolutely universal genius has never been known, every leader remains a leader only within a narrow groove and for a short stretch of way; for the most part, he too is merely a follower.

Whichever way we look at the situation, the basic fact stands out that the individual and the body politic are linked in a complementary relationship and thus "covered" by the same cosmic law which the new physics declares to be the most universal thus far known.[4]

Although the logic of complementarity has at last given us the means of integrating social science into general science, it is, unfortunately, not so facile as is the one-eyed everyday logic prevailing within the cramped dimensions within which most men live. Complementarity is, so to speak, a multivalent, non-Euclidian logic. Everyday logic may suffice for the trifling problems of normal individual life, but applied to the quasi-universal dimensions of life-as-a-whole, or merely the body politic, it has always proved a failure. There were few shrewder logical minds of this sort than Thomas Hobbes (1588–1679), whose one-eyed casuistry almost succeeded in standing the world on its head. In his *Leviathan* he began by setting up individual man as free and sovereign and wound up with making him a helpless slave of the absolute state. Using the strict mechanical logic of the flatlands of rationalism so alien to life, he could not without loss of his logical integrity help enslaving man.

STATISM

Regarding the dangers of absolutism, we can be brief in view of the shocking illustrations contemporary history has provided. We can confine ourselves to showing that at least some of the results of statism are not accidental, but inevitable and specific, because they arise from disregard of specific laws of nature.

Whereas individualism is the fruit of extreme somatic development, the state, representing the point of farthest advance in the integration of the species, is for this reason intimately linked to the species aspect of man. Hence the abuses and excesses of the absolute state inevitably have as their concomitant a general, often official, bending back toward instinctual species activities—to beastliness.

We find, therefore, that under all forms of statism crude animal behavior obtains a new lease on life. In European history the final victory of absolutist Roman law was accompanied by the most shameless spectacle of public and private dissoluteness, moral corruption and crass, fetid animalism. Always, under such conditions, social development stagnates or regresses, though externalities may for some time hide the internal decay.

How, more specifically, does it become apparent that absolutism is a throwback and disregard of basic law?

While in great periods of individualism the mind feverishly explores the farthest reaches of thought, under state absolutism to think independently becomes a crime. Since the state as such cannot think, individual thought, too, must be jealously suppressed. And with individual thought and activity reduced to a minimum, species activities, which mean the lowest common behavioral denominator, experience a sharp recrudescence.

Always, therefore, state absolutism is accompanied by a partial collapse, or the complete deterioration, of those spheres of life which at their best represent animal instincts sublimated into ethical domains.

In the reproductive field, a widespread, almost official promiscuity is one of the standard features of pronounced statism. The sexual chaos under Spartan totalitarianism has already been mentioned. Imperial Rome was hardly better, nor the Roman Church at the height of her absolutism. Under Louis XIV of France, his successors and imitators, the "divine right" of the king included nothing less than access to every woman of the realm. The despot David of Judah displayed similar tendencies. Plato, in his *Republic*, a semicommunistic totalitarian Utopia, proposed total promiscuity among the ruling elite and the abolition of the family; and Marx in his gospel of salvation copied Plato on this point. Sexual "liberation" was directly celebrated in the early days of the Bolshevik revolution. The drastic revision of morals in the downward direction under Mussolini and Hitler is notorious. And finally, the absolutist character of army life seems to have the same effect the world over.

In the alimentary field and economic life in general, despite all centralized "planning," absolutist regimes tend to get equally disorganized, because the guarantee of one's daily bread and other needs no longer depends on willingness to work, but on submission to state doctrine, the "party line." The result generally is that "planned economy" begets black markets and other economic evils.

Decay is even more apparent in the field of defense (in the widest sense of the term). Nowhere is life so insecure as where the security of the state is the only consideration. Nowhere is the individual so persistently on the defensive, living under conditions resembling those of a cornered or hunted beast, as in collectivist countries. Murder, the starvation and torturing to death of thousands, the expulsion from their homes and the slavery of millions become a matter of course.

Under every form of absolutism and in all instinctual domains and their social embodiments, what we called the creative "slack" field becomes tense. The systematic creation of tension, internal and external, a "war of nerves," is stereotype. It is on almost universal fear alone that the absolute state can build its might. To keep suspicion, tension, terror, snooping and denunciation at a high pitch, official fear-creating organs are instituted, usually under the name "organs of security." Such were Mussolini's Black Shirts, the Gestapo, the Soviet OGPU and NKVD, the papal Inquisition, and similar institutions among such "religious totalitarianisms" as Calvin's Geneva and the early New England Puritanism.

The worst of totalitarianism is that in the end "planned economy" (or "planned salvation," in the case of ecclesiastic absolutism) always encroaches upon the field of justice. It ends by being planned jurisdiction, with predetermined verdicts, machine-made sentences delivered by "packed" courts and "picked" juries.

Thus we see that even in its degeneracy the absolute state corroborates the laws of nature. Just as excessive individualism, its opposite, statism, always ends in beastliness and general dissoluteness. Extremes meet. State absolutism is in effect often nothing other than the aberrant individualism of a small clique of poseurs pretending to have sopped up into their systems the very essence of the state. *L'Etat, c'est Nous.*

The end is always the end of freedom. And since "freedom" is essentially a shorthand symbol for the evolutionary possibilities in a "slack" field of polarities, the trend toward any monopolarity is always a symptom of decadence. There are no exceptions among historical or present-day examples; there are only degrees of absolutist miscarriage, on the individual pole or the state pole.

15

THE CENTRAL PROBLEMS OF POLITICS

INDIVIDUAL and state are not the only political factors. Wherever social development has progressed beyond the elementary stages, the body politic becomes stratified into permanent or temporary classes, and individuals are organized in groups representing a great variety of overlapping interests—material, intellectual, religious, etc. Politics hence becomes group or class politics, and the standing of the individual is generally determined by his standing within the group. As a matter of principle, though, the fundamental complementary relationship persists, between individual and group, between groups and the state, and between various groups. Since none is ever self-sufficient, none can become absolute without catastrophic results. It is precisely for this reason that all civilizations have made attempts to regulate such interdependencies by law. The very fact of the rational insight into these conditions, however imperfect, sets off civilizations from primitive societies.

THE NATURE OF LAW

The realization that human law is part of the law of nature is as old as is the institution of law itself. Often it was assumed to have been handed down directly by God, or a god, or by a divine king, and what understanding of it man could gain depended on how

much the capricious gods were willing to reveal. In this regard the
Germanic tribes were rather exceptional. To them, too, human
law was part of the order of nature, but they knew it would never
be revealed to them by divine condescension. On the contrary,
they considered it to be man's foremost duty in this world to *find*
the law. Theirs was therefore, in the fullest sense of the term, a
"scientific" attitude, and it can hardly be accidental that the cradle
area of modern science is approximately congruous with the area
over which those tribes dispersed: from Great Britain and Scandi-
navia to the Mediterranean, from the Atlantic to the interior of
Russia. These tribes even anticipated the central concept of modern physics. Whereas Roman law, for instance, was concrete,
static and pedestrian, a law of persons and of things, Germanic
law was from the beginning abstract, dynamic, functional, always
expressing complementary interdependences in pairs of concepts:
right and duty, law and freedom, king and people, sword side and
distaff side, etc. The accent was never on persons or things, but on
the dynamic relations between them.

The great difficulty which the belief in "natural law" encounters
in our day lies in the circumstance that nothing as awesomely
demonstrates the gulf between physical-organic nature and the
mental sphere as do the differences between the laws of science
and those of the body politic. They seem beyond comparison.
Nevertheless, the fundamental principles behind them are the
same. If they were based on radically different fundamentals, natural science could never have borrowed its basic vocabulary and
methods from the older legal domain, not without becoming guilty
of unscientific analogy. But the borrowing was natural and justified. For the method of establishing law—physical, biological,
social—depending as it does on certain common features of all
evolutionary phases, is everywhere the same. In all these fields true
law, or good law (even physicists use this expression), is *found*,
not made. Finding the law is based on *search* and *research*, the
study of the *facts* of a *case*, of the *evidence*. It requires *judgment*
in the drawing of *conclusions*. In every instance the final crystal-

lization out of such efforts is a general (never absolute) rule called the *law*, or the *formula*, henceforth to be applied in all like cases. A successful science derived from unscientific principles, or tenets not soundly rooted in a natural order, would be the weirdest of all ironies.

Beyond this common basis of method and vocabulary, the law and science soon came to a parting of the ways. Physical science deals with extremely elementary situations. Even biology is relatively simple compared with the dilemma of the mind trying to understand itself, which is the dilemma of all social sciences. The worst was that, the more science triumphed in its conquest of nature, the more the men of the law became obsessed with the notion that their laws had nothing whatsoever to do with nature and promptly awarded themselves a brief for arbitrariness. While objective science and technology opened numerous new fields of exploitation during the nineteenth century, during the same period they were accompanied on the political scene by little else but brazen legislation in favor of the ruthless few, the dispensers of political bribe. Laws, instead of being impartially ascertained, were more and more contrived. The law*maker* became a recognized human breed where once he would have been considered a faker. Objective science still does not recognize the breed. Not unjustly has it been said that most civilized countries are today kept from collapsing by the means provided by science and technology rather than by their legal institutions.

To this must be added that the legal mind has lagged far behind scientific-technological developments—perhaps because, being so much older, it is more sluggish, perhaps because it has more and more substituted for the initial faith in a natural law a system of synthetic formalism obviating mental effort, search and exploration. The result is what one philosopher of the law called legal vacuums.[1] These are most obvious in those social fields owing their existence to recent technological advances, especially in management-labor relations. Although the law, by sanctioning collective bargaining, has recognized the complementary nature of employer-employee relationships, it has remained purblind in face of the fact that no single management-labor group is self-sufficient and autonomous, but that all are interlocked into one single functional system. The legal vacuums thus left are the breeding grounds of racketeers. Unless we find a legal solution for the problem of the total functional integration in an industrial world we are destined sooner or later to succumb to these defects.

DEMOCRACY AND ECONOMICS

In turning now to a few of the foremost politico-legal questions of modern civilization, it is meet to recall the extreme youth of this male phase of human history. Its continuous troubles may be taken as proof that the problem of political civilization has not yet been solved even as regards some of its fundamentals. For a century and a half now most of the advanced thinkers have held democracy to be the ideal and final mold in which civilization will ultimately reach its perfection. In its basic tenets it does indeed embody the principle of complementarity and therefore natural law. Yet the sudden reappearance after the first World War of extreme forms of dictatorship has raised a host of questions. Of these I will take up only one: have the democracies really proved to be the luminaries they believe themselves to be? The only answers that suggest themselves are in the negative.

There is no doubt in my mind that Lincoln's formulation of democracy as "government of the people, by the people, for the people" goes to the heart of the matter. This is, however, no more than an ideal programmatic statement and hence the pointing out of a problem. The main questions now are: (1) have we realized the ideal? (2) how far is the principle really applicable? Here doubts set in. Like the priest who felt like treating himself to a pullet during Lent and, to soothe his conscience, prefaced the eating of it by saying, "I herewith christen you carp," we have applied the name of democracy to a good many things that are something else.

Basically, civilization means mental speciation, the branching off of a body of rational (civilized) minds from a nonrational (primitive) mass at a time which on the evolutionary scale was but a moment ago. It is therefore not to be expected that the interval has been sufficient for all to catch up. The nature of the most popular media of entertainment, to mention but one indicator, is proof that the primitives among us still constitute a vast majority. Nor can we doubt that they are indeed necessary to every civilization. This new mode of social organization was from the beginning based on the complementarity of leaders and followers (which is hardly the case in vegetative primitivity).

With this universal fact, then, is also given the foremost political problem of all civilizations, in other words, its basic legal question. For if all men were leaders, there could be no followers, civilization would dissolve into chaos, and in a chaos there are no leaders. And if all men were followers (of primitive traditions), i.e., if leaders were lacking, civilizations could never arise. Both are absolutely necessary, but, this constituting the basic legal question, the relationship of leaders and followers must be legally formulated. Tradition has always accorded the leaders certain privileges, or, more precisely, the leaders at first simply arrogated privileges without compensating their followers, probably because in the very beginning of every civilization the "followers" were an unwilling and recalcitrant mass of slaves. Democracy is simply the formal recognition of the complementary relationship of leaders and led, and the restitution by the leaders of certain privileges to their followers. The problem thus boils down to that of the distribution of both privileges and obligations, or rights and duties, among leaders and followers. Here every civilization, every state, must find its own appropriate solution.

With this in mind let us turn to some aspects of present-day democracy. It is a familiar argument that true, or pure, democracy is impossible on a large scale. This contention contains, telescoped into each other, two different facts: first, that there have never been enough humans constitutionally fit to organize and maintain a true democracy on a very large scale; second, that there are very many who find it personally the more profitable the less democracy there is. A political democracy which does not involve economic democracy is of course a pseudo-democracy. This follows with absolute necessity from what was said in Chapter 14, from the evolutionary fact, namely, that *the individual's attributes and achievements are never his own exclusively,* but to a far greater extent than we generally realize those of the population of which he is a part. This scientific certainty by itself contains the moral death sentence of "economic feudalism," the power of the "captains of industry" to remunerate themselves according to their own inordinate estimate of their worth and at the cost of the populace.

For illustration take any corporate behemoth. First, it does not exist alone on the strength of a few organizers; the customers are an integral part of it. Producer and consumer form a complementary pair. Second, the organizers and managers were not their own creators, but upshots of the gene pool of the nation and of its social traditions. Third, the principles applied in the industry are rarely its own discoveries, but are found by scientists and as scientific ideas are for the most part in the public domain. Fourth, an industry like the motor industry, e.g., flourishes mainly thanks to the roads built by various government agencies. Fifth, the working capital of most industries is not really their own, but made up from the following sources: withheld wages, excess of prices over production cost, stockholders' investments, individual savings collected through banks, savings invested by pension trusts and life insurance companies.

The industry itself therefore is only a minor (though the most visible) part of an immensely ramifying setup virtually comprising the whole nation. Yet the major part of its net earnings (three-fifths, on the average) is withheld from the financial supporters for reinvestment or expansion (partly justified in a growing economy) or as more or less hidden bonuses. In principle, therefore, the system is not too different from that of medieval serfdom, in which the great beneficiaries were the holders of fiefs, i.e., the "managers" of landed property not really their own.

Economically, then, we are far from democracy. The main reason no doubt is the shift of accent from politics to business. This entails two consequences: (1) politics is handed over to delegated agents, becoming "representative" and hence a business itself; (2) business being undemocratic per se, even politics is bound to become as undemocratic as the business interests it represents. The absolutist tendencies of the system are familiar. The complementarities of the body social are in danger of being dissolved because the unearned profit of the few in the strategic positions becomes the driving motive; means become ends.

Evidently, the basic problem here is of an ethical nature, and ethic is nothing else but the recognition of complementarity as the most fundamental law of nature. Even that one-time savior of capitalism, John Maynard Keynes, saw that the great moral problem of our age is "the habitual appeal to the money motive in nine-tenths of the activities of life" and called capitalism "one of those semicriminal, semipathological propensities" which ought to be taken in hand by psychiatrists rather than by economists. The obvious innuendo is that the disease is not confined to capitalists but virtually generic of the human species. Some of the criticism implied in the above brief analysis of corporate life therefore applies to labor as well, which generally has as little regard for the body social as a whole as the managers, though it "sponges" as much on society as the latter.

In recent decades, though, some changes for the better have taken place. Classical economic theory declared the insecurities of anarchy to be of the essence of capitalistic progress. During slumps of the market temperature life was supposed to go underground. With the cold-bloodedness of cold-blooded animals those who had accumulated enough to weather the freeze considered it none of their business if those whom they had kept from doing likewise perished. This was "the survival of the fittest," a new interpretation of "the Laws of Nature and of Nature's God," and nothing could be done about it.

But during the great crisis of the thirties and under the influence of Keynes we were heretics enough to do something. It was as if somebody had remembered Claude Bernard's "the constancy of the internal milieu is the prerequisite of a free life." If another metaphor be permitted, this was the beginning of a "warm-blooded" political economy maintained by social stabilizers. These latter, to be sure, are still far from perfect, as witness the wage-price spiral, which nobody has as yet had the moral courage to do anything about and which is an indication that our social system is still out of control. Nevertheless, what stabilizers we have seem to have done away with the grossest business fluctuations.

All this is recognition, however vague, of economic complementarity, the interdependence of all and everything. No man grows rich solely on his own merit (for instance as a hermit on an island). The millions of the population are the more important factor in any accumulated wealth. But neither, of course, would the millions be of any use without economic leaders. Here again the basic universal law is manifest and implies that there is after all such a thing as a natural economic system and that at length none other can survive. Also, a natural system in the sense here suggested can be the only valid ethical system. We know from experience that neither abstract philosophical ethic nor theologically motivated ethic has ever proved of any use in economic life. There was a time when the Church was the most ruthless "robber baron" syndicate, and at the end of the nineteenth century there were still Protestant theologians who declared God to be on the side of the rich. A natural economy based on the theory of complementarity offers the greatest challenge to the economists, most of whom still seem addicted to the niceties of academic boondoggling. In practice a natural economy resolves itself, of course, into the problem of a fair distribution of rewards, which no doubt would often appear unfair to those on top as well as those at the bottom. It is doubtful whether the problem can be solved under the traditional "free enterprise" concept, which follows essentially the might-is-right principle.

To prevent misconceptions, be it said that the natural economy here envisaged can never mean socialism if by socialism is understood a state economy. Evolution always means progressive self-differentiation and the integrative complementarity of the products of differentiation. This is not identical with merger, whereas socialism is the merger of politics and economy.

We have here come upon a new and very essential complementarity in social evolution: that of politics and economics. To be fruitful the two must certainly be integrated, but they should neither be confused nor, much less, amalgamated, for the same reason, evidently, that in politics we insist on the familiar separation of governmental powers. The relationship of government and business is, after all, but a somewhat different aspect of the complementarity of state and individual, or of the state and groups. They fulfill different functions; for the state, let us remind ourselves, represents the farthest point in the process of species integration, whereas the individual is the decisive evolutionary instigator.

The separation of government and business hence conforms to natural principles, but this conveys on neither side complete autonomy. It may still justify the state's taking over economic domains which enterprisers neglect or have muddled up, and it might not prevent business from showing initiative where the government has none. By and large, though, integrated separation of their functions represents the truly "organic" and evolutionarily most productive solution. Integration here means of course regulation of the functions of both sides and their mutualities by law and for the benefit of the body politic as a whole rather than of individuals and groups. However, and this point needs emphasis, the best law is useless when applied to a population unable to live up to it. Since legal machinations can carry us no further than our biopsychological nature allows, this would indicate that sooner or later a biological policy may become the most pressing need for a genuine social upward movement. Our "nature" has so far permitted us to overcome the insanity of the blood feud but not yet the criminality of willful economic havoc, at the top as well as at the bottom of the social pyramid, though it generally affects the body politic more profoundly than does even the murder of a President.

CONSTITUTIONAL PROBLEMS

Even in our noneconomic institutions, i.e., in "pure" politics, we are probably farther from democracy than we think. There is, to begin with, the problem of "representative government," already touched upon above. It is generally conceded to be a substitute for the "direct" democracy held to be out of question on a large scale, but found, for instance, among some Greek city-states, some small Swiss cantons with their *Landsgemeinde*, and the New England town meeting. Napoleon Bonaparte, that overadulated political brigand, was perhaps more clear-sighted than some of our Founding Fathers when he spoke of "the representative system which destroys the essential attributes of a republic" (not to mention democracy). Has there ever been a period of our history when the federal legislature, or that of any state, was truly representative? The emphatic answer is No. Legislatures have never represented anything but powerful blocs, and the executives have often connived with them. Oligarchy has been our predominant form of government, and under Roosevelt II and Johnson II we have sometimes been close to monarchy.

From an evolutionary point of view to ask whether "pure" or "direct" democracy is possible on dimensions larger than microscopic is like asking whether a mouse can become an elephant. Literally, of course, it cannot, as the Romans found out. Nevertheless, the elephant, like the mouse, is a vertebrate and a mammal. Both share the same fundamental constitution. As a matter of principle, therefore, we probably cannot *a priori* deny the possibility of true democracy on a very large, say, continental, scale. The difficulty arises from the fact that, whereas the elephant is constituted of nothing but elephant cells, all hereditarily endowed with the qualities necessary to an elephant, modern political theory is still under the spell of the magical faith that a democratic mammoth can be synthesized, as it were, of "cells" taken from almost any kind of animal—from bacilli to rats, mindless chickens and cheerful songbirds, strutting peacocks, sloths, sacred beefs and voracious wolves. The result is that the various non-democratic elements—the pushers, self-seekers and agents of narrow group interests—become represented out of proportion.[2] The nineteenth century was the classical age for this sort of pseudo-democracy.

Even under the best of circumstances the problem of representation is complex. Where legislatures represent a mosaic of local districts, the state or nation frequently has no representation. That is to say, the complementarity of whole and parts is in abeyance and legislation gets warped, biased in favor of some localities, social strata, or economic fields, while others, to use old-fashioned terms, pay tribute to them, i.e., become political subjects of the first. The Silver Purchase Act and the Depletion Allowance (which exempts 27½ percent of oil income from taxation) are the most notorious examples. Some farm legislation is also of this nature in that it is designed to favor the rich landholders and to eliminate the small farmer. In all such cases legislation becomes pure politics in the worst sense, the amanuensis of special interests, in which the interests of the body politic as a whole are of no concern to anybody.

A move to restore the complementarity of government and the governed was undertaken with the introduction of the referendum, the initiative and the right of recall. The results in those of our states which have adopted some or all of these measures have, however, not been very satisfactory. It was discovered that even such remedies can be abused by selfish or bigoted interests. Under our present national constitution, referendum, initiative and recall are still impossible, which makes the federal government much less democratic than state governments.

The constitutional provision regarding the separation of powers —legislative, executive and judiciary—furnishes the most instructive example of the recognition of basic natural law in the political domain. As a formal feature of governmental organization it can-

not be too highly valued. Its introduction in 1787 must be regarded as one of the significant leaps forward in political evolution
and political insight. It was a novelty which could never have been
derived from any other source than the philosophy of natural law.
Here we have a triple complementarity arising by means of specializing differentiation from a single, once unitary, power resid-
ing in the monarch. If we take further into consideration that this
triune complementarity is, theoretically at least, conceived of as
the articulation of the people, we have a quadrivium of powers
derived from a basic unit: popular sovereignty.

In practice, though, the ideal theoretical foundation has always
assumed another face and become much impaired. One of these
impairments (the nonrepresentative character of the legislature)
has already been dealt with. Nor has the situation usually been
better in the two other governmental divisions. Party politics, the
often imbecile hullabaloo which traditionally has become part of
presidential elections, make it virtually impossible to get a man
into the White House who truly represents the nation, except
(sometimes) in foreign affairs. Because of the generally nonrepresentative character of the Congress, the executive has been forced
to take over a good deal of legislation, not always in the best
interest of the country. Congress then either becomes the familiar
"rubber stamp" or, if it has a will of its own, there is a deadlock.
Furthermore, the monarchic buildup of the presidency under
Roosevelt II, with the superabundance of funds available to the
chief executive, generally means that a vote against a White House
measure cuts off the district or state of a No-voting member of
Congress from presidential appropriations, since these latter are
traditionally used as "pork barrels" rather than according to actual
need. And finally, the interpretation of the law by the Supreme
Court is also a form of legislation. In the last analysis, the law
always is what the Court says it is, so that again the complementarity of the three branches of government as well as that of government and people is disregarded in favor of virtual dictatorship.
But all this is probably still unavoidable in a young and extremely

heterogeneous nation. Much greater political maturity would be required of the nation to relieve the Supreme Court as well as the Presidency of some of their dictatorial powers.

By and large, then, the fundamental intentions of the Constitution have remained ideals rather than something followed in practice. The reasons are fairly obvious. The Founders had in mind a rather homogeneous population of politically wide-awake men. The Pilgrims, e.g., had come over here to create a Protestant version of the City of God. Later immigrants came for other reasons, at best economic ones. Nineteenth-century mass immigration particularly meant a radical change of the original situation. It derived its strength chiefly from regions of Europe where the people never enjoyed political rights, where those who attempted reforms were often ruthlessly eliminated and where, therefore, the polity of the ruling class amounted to a breeding policy aimed at the creation of a "pure culture" of submissive masses, largely unthinking and without innate political talents.

Accordingly, relatively few of the descendants of those immigrant masses have constructively contributed to our political institutions. There are, indeed, reasons to believe that the most ardent promoters of mass immigration had no designs other than to use the masses as a pretext to divert the course of the nation's development away from the course envisioned by the Founders.

There is another reason for this trend. It was a great piece of good fortune that the birth of the United States coincided with an age of Western history when political philosophy intensely preoccupied the foremost thinkers. The laying of the country's foundations could thus, as a matter of course, be left to the best available brains. But before the new nation could fully work out the practical forms in which the basic concepts were to be realized, science and technology moved into the forefront of intellectual interest, absorbing the outstanding talents. New fields, new frontiers of the mind, always offer the greatest challenge and appeal most to the creative elements of a population. The political field thus fell into the hands of humdrum men and mere exploiters.

Even many of our Presidents have been men of average, or even lesser caliber, men without ideas of their own, though skillful self-promoters and players of the political "game." The suspicion (it is as yet no more) is even warranted that the present high-pressure movement to make "democracy more democratic" is one of these games. It may sound like heresy, but the truth is that universal suffrage is in no way identical with democracy. The more the right to vote was extended in ancient Rome, the more it made dictatorship an entrenched institution. The plain scientific fact that a nation's political standards and its potential evolutionary rank depend in the last analysis on its ethnic composition, i.e., its gene pool, has never dawned on us as a nation. Yet to think otherwise in this "scientific age" would seem to be ingenuous, and to preach otherwise, demagogism.

I see no other remedy for this decline of politics, of which one hears from all "free" nations, but to introduce some scientific notions into the field. Among these, it is worth repeating, ultimately (once science is spiritually mature enough, which today it is not by a long shot) will be that of a biological policy giving due regard to genetics and mental speciation. Until then, schools might become of some help if we can educate the educators, especially the educational psychologists, the professors of economics and law. Traditional religion, unfortunately, offers little hope. Its social concepts, if and where it has any, are still muddled, rudiments of magic primitivity, and down the ages (particularly where it was too "otherworldly," hardened in a hierarchy or in an "eternal" law) its talent for secular pimping has been phenomenal.

POLITICS AND SCIENCE

The need for a scientifically oriented political life is implicit in the fact that political civilization is but the youngest phase in the evolution of life and presently the most active evolutionary front, even if that front has now advanced from the once purely organic level to one at least partly mental. Mind is as good a part of nature as anything.

The crucial deficiency of politics as we know it rests in its being almost exclusively based on the two instincts of *self*-preservation. The state, however, from the evolutionary point of view, represents the stage of farthest advance of *species* integration, wherefore, in large measure at least, it ought to be determined by the self-transcending instinct of *species preservation* and its sublimates —which can generally be subsumed under the concept of ethics. The truth, though, is that the concerns of the commonwealth have become the captive monopoly of the agents of utter egotism. As the leading advocate of congressional reform, Senator Joseph S. Clark, put it, it is in the legislatures "where vested interest lobbies run riot, where conflict of interest rides unchecked . . . where the Nineteenth Century still reigns supreme in committees, where ignorance is often at a premium and wisdom at a discount."[3]

But the problem of social and political evolution is scientific by nature for the reason of its being part of the new, consciously mental, evolution, also founded on complementarity. Moreover, if up to now civilizations—feudalistic-agrarian or bourgeois-commercial—have as a matter of course been dominated by their creators, it becomes a legitimate inference that a scientific civilization ultimately must be managed and guided by scientific minds, not by the survivors of an atavistic orientation. Few are aware how fundamentally different the two mentalities are. Whereas science strives for a unification of its concepts by reducing many of its older laws to fewer and more universal ones, the political legalism of the still dominant commercial spirit is constantly enlarging and thickening its jungle[4] and at the same time ignoring the legal vacuums which the economic exploitation of scientific gains has created.

We must concede, however, that this situation is abetted by the circumstance that even the majority of the scientifically trained have little or no understanding of the evolutionary significance of science. They can see in it no more than a fashionable way of taking part in the economic free-for-all—just as the commercial world is largely a backward-looking congeries of those to whom business is but a sort of feudalistic status and power seeking.

The reasons why the scientific world as a whole has hardly troubled to understand the vital implications of the new physics are fairly obvious. Even scientists have so far discovered how to achieve practical results mainly by investigating causal-deterministic connections. And the truth is, of course, that the world as most of us know it is predominantly deterministic, and that our "understanding," our concept of what "makes sense," is almost entirely confined to narrow cause-and-effect relations. But the revolutionary achievement of the new physics is precisely the discovery of a *more fundamental* nondeterministic side of nature. Mechanistic cause and effect alone simply do not make for *organization*, certainly not *vital* organization,[5] but produce only sporadic events. The one evolutionarily significant principle is the new physics' complementarity, which, in the world of the living, probably means the complementarity of microphysical indeterminacy and mechanistic determinacy. This alone makes possible an organic whole and permits a measure of freedom.

Politics and the law are still remote from scientific concepts. In politics in particular expediency and arbitrariness have often been the only "principles." We shall therefore never extricate ourselves from the chronic crises, which make up almost the entire history of civilization, unless we find ways and means of removing politics from the sway of those who use their "minds" merely to pander to their instincts. The paramount issue of civilization is whether or not we are prepared to draw the final consequences from evolution (inasfar as it relates to man) and willing to give supremacy not to animal undercurrents but to what has from the beginning been the making of man: ethico-rational thought. In other words, if one be permitted to take the long view, the only alternative to perennial chaos would seem to be to hand politics over to what, for the lack of a better term, must be called dispassionate, objective science (in the very widest and serenest meaning of the term).[6] Where everything depends on integration, science, the knowledge of the integrative processes of nature, should have priority over politics, the fishing in the troubled waters of disintegration.

I realize that to express such thoughts is to step into a hornets' nest. Conservatism is an inbuilt part of every human establishment, as it is of hornets' nests. They all dislike having their evolutionary inertia disturbed, and even revolutionary systems, so-called, become conservative as soon as established. That is overwhelmingly true even of Marxism, which claims to be *the* social and governmental science of the future. We need waste no time over this claim. Nevertheless, it is perhaps not gratuitous to point out the fact that Marxism seems to be the first historic instance where at least the *ideal* of government according to scientific principles was recognized (even if Marxism itself is not a science by any impartial standards). By contrast, we, with our actually more scientific common-law and natural-law foundation, still convulse at the notion that government and politics should ever be anything else than what they are today: legalized Saturnalia of passions and opinionateness.

This should not be misunderstood to mean that modern basic physics has made it possible for a committee of experts to work out the details of a genuine political science. We are still far from that. What is required, in the first place, is a revolution in thought. The nonpolitical side of our civilization is the gift almost exclusively of the physical, to a lesser degree of the biological, sciences. By the very fact that we call ours, in the absolute sense, a *scientific civilization* we proclaim that the achievements of science have far outstripped in importance the politico-legal machinations. But precisely because of this radical shift of emphasis in the nature of modern life it would hardly be safe indefinitely to leave its guidance to "old-brain" politicians. Only the creative minds of an age, never the dominant element of the evolutionary yesteryear, are fit to be its leading spirits.

This must be already apparent to any who, at a luncheon or smoker, ever sat down with a congeries of men of undistinguished prosperity, the very element that sets the tone in politics. In such circles even scientific genius like Einstein's may become everybody's laughingstock,[7] for the same reason that at one time of history the saints were the laughingstock of the princes of the church. In the same rubric belong the increasingly frequent attempts of politico-legal minds to "put scientists in their place." Their utterances are often surprisingly similar to the haughty condescension of feudalists a few hundred years ago vis-à-vis the rising economic bourgeoisie.

It appears, though, to be a fact of biological as well as of social evolution that the rise to dominance of the youngest order is of the very essence of evolution. Only the incipient scientific order is in the fullest extent beginning to appreciate man's intellectual powers and to translate into one concrete form or another thought untainted by animal instinct. It has within a century and a half revolutionized society, whereas politics has hardly brought forth a single new idea since the eighteenth century laid the theoretical foundations of modern democracy.

Fortunately, the situation is not hopeless. It was pointed out that science borrowed its basic methods and vocabulary from the older discipline of the law. Both were born of the same spirit and hold *justice* to observed or recorded *facts* to be of supreme importance. There are sporadic signs that legal thought too is trying to emulate the exactness and impartiality of science. Moreover, most civilized nations at least attempt to fill judiciary offices with men expected to be governed in their decisions by unbiased standards, not by their material interests or animal instincts. Insofar as they fulfill these expectations, and insofar as the law they administer allows, such judges are acting in the spirit of objective science. There is room for improvement even in this domain. But who could deny that of all branches of government, jurisdiction is today by far the least objectionable and the most dependable? The thought, therefore, should not be too outlandish that someday even politics might become the equal of jurisdiction in dignity and objectivity, though none of us now living may hope to see that day.

16

FREEDOM AND THE MIND

THE preceding chapter could be summed up in the statement
that the central problem of sociopolitical evolution is that
of mental maturity, of the ability to employ to the fullest
extent possible the interdependence of all individuals, all groups,
and ultimately the entire human species. All are but minor focal
points, or focal areas, of a bewildering maze of dynamic complementarities linking into a single whole all life. We may never
know the whole, nor can we understand an individual except as an
aspect of a population. Quite definitely, from an evolutionary point
of view the vital entity is the population, not the individual.

In view of this state of things the most hopelessly fossil concept
is that of the "free and independent" individual. Where it still
flourishes it is generally virulent and parasitic. As has been amply
demonstrated, the very mind harboring this notion was fashioned
on the social loom by millions of other minds around it, and by
the thoughts of other millions preceding it in evolution.

The primordial group spirit, out of which individual minds
have gradually differentiated, is the matrix particularly of ethics,
which for this reason remains the conservative binding element of
social systems, whereas rationality is the dynamic evolutionary
agent and also, in its negative aspect, taken as an absolute, a dis-
integrating factor. Normal social evolution is possible only where,
and as long as, centripetal ethic and centrifugal reason remain

241

balanced, integral factors within the social whole. Here as elsewhere a new and higher level of evolution is reached only by the "coincidence of opposites." Mental, like physical, maturity is the readiness to recognize an opposite as the complement necessary for a fuller life.

The sociopolitical evolution of our immediate future will therefore be determined in the first place by the extent to which our ethic, long slighted during a period of extreme but narrow rationalism, can catch up with and become one with reason. Later in this chapter we shall see what extraordinary fruits this "marriage" has borne in one particular domain; but first, having so often merely touched upon the subject of ethics, we must briefly review its role in evolution in a more connected way than was so far possible.

ETHICS

The term "ethics" is our verbal symbol for something incomprehensible which began to regulate interdependencies between members of a multi-individual system the moment physiological regulation became inadequate. Even if we recognize that complementarity is also the basic form of ethics, and ethics, therefore, is complementarity risen to consciousness, we still have not really explained it. A development has come full circle. We are again face to face with a *prima causa,* and first causes are probably never explicable.

Only in the sense of ethics as primordial complementarity risen to consciousness are we justified in saying that man alone is a moral creature. In lower orders of life an unconscious psychophysiological ethos achieves the same normative ends as human ethics. As a matter of etymological fact, "ethos" and "ethics" originally meant nothing more than character, behavior; and with all creatures and without exception, these are manifestations of organic constitution. In the strictest sense, every atom, every bacillus has, if not its conscious ethics, certainly an unconscious ethos. An ethos is the quintessence of every kind of order or system in the world. One might indeed subsume all evolution in the statement that what actually evolves is the ethos. Only where this is the case can we truly speak of "anagenesis," the actual advance of life, while changes not accompanied by such a widening and ascension of the ethos are mere "cladogenesis," diversification on the same level, without any actual rise in "biological living standards."

Human ethics, then, is the exact functional equivalent of the physiological ethos and evolved in much the same way as the conscious mind evolved out of the subconscious processes of automatic physiology. However, whereas it is a theoretical point whether we regard man as the only ethical animal or the only consciously ethical one, it remains a matter of utmost practical importance that our ethics must be human, relative to man, and that any other is bound to fail. It is plain nonsense, of which many of the biologically unwise from Solomon to the official guardians of Marxism have been guilty, to refer to the ant and the honeybee as our moral peers. But, alas, we cannot imitate them, even if we wanted to, without stripping ourselves of every shred of humanity, Our ethos must be strictly human.

Because in man alone unconscious psychological or physiological regulation of interindividual behavior has become subject to the rule of the conscious ethico-rational mind, his social problems can no longer hope for satisfactory solutions under the prompting of the physiological instincts. In fact, the human nervous system is so organized as to make the two poles, the mental and the instinctual, mutually exclusive, or nearly so. This is why you are not likely to achieve the squaring of the circle at the height of an amatory interlude, nor make crucial strategic decisions in the heat of combat. For the same cause, reasoning tainted by instinct is anything but pure reasoning and by nature unfit to solve problems concerning the body politic. Such reasoning has always been called unethical.

Ethics, then, as a manifestation of primal complementarity, is a universal phenomenon. Only in being conscious of it is man unique, and nothing could be more shallow than the old religious notion of ethics being implanted in man, and him alone, by other-worldly magic. Like everything else, it is a flower of the evolution-ary process.

Even the history of statutory law corroborates this. It first appears as a method of compensation or retribution for bodily harm done: murder, injury, poisoning and rape.[1] Primitive law is always of the type of "an eye for an eye, a tooth for a tooth." That is to say, it is explicitly an attempt to remedy, by the crudest and most naïve means, a disturbed physical or physiological equilibrium (the physiological ethos) in the body social. Pristine law thus has lucidly held fast for us the moment when the automatic organic ethos gave way to the radically different conscious social ethic.

That this process took place particularly under the tutelage of the optical sense and made human consciousness essentially a matter of mental vision has been sufficiently stressed. It is the fact that vision is preeminently a relational sense and thought the conscious formulation of relations which enabled man ever better to realize social potentials. Yet the organic basis of social life persists, and with it the physiology of the instincts, though it is always thought which administers their affairs and humanizes them. Their proper functioning depends on our conscious mastery of the complexities involved in them, and on our ability constantly to readjust ourselves to the changes in the social equilibrium. And because the equilibrium is the result of carefully balanced mutual relations of all with all, however indirect, and a disturbance of the equilibrium affects all, every tampering with it under the prompting of instinct becomes detrimental, unethical. Where all are concerned, individual motives, or group motives, may not dominate. In short, the solution of social problems, depending on "pure thought," must be "purely mental," ethical no less than rational. Where the ethical side is slighted, the purely rational part becomes malignant, or even ruinous.

In the grand perspective of life's evolution, physiology and ethic, then, denote successive, radically different, but overlapping and interacting phases. They cannot be cleanly separated, as you can never separate man's physical entity from his mental and social existence; and there is for this reason no ethical experience without its concrete organic concomitant. All unethical behavior on the part of one constitutes an upsetting of the physiological equilibrium of others. It acts like a poison, as is evident from the fact that an individual can be morally wounded to death or to insanity. Every unethical act, even if not on the statute books, is a criminal act, never without harm to someone.

As is well known even to the casual observer, the lack of a binding ethic in our present world is especially obvious in power structures of all kinds, bureaucratic hierarchies—in brief, in "pecking orders." Power, as others have often pointed out, is by nature unethical, no matter in what hallowed disguise it appears, and has seldom bred anything but corruption. It is a subject which scholars approach warily, not only because it cannot be treated without treading on countless toes, but also because it defies traditional methods of treatment. Adolf A. Berle, in his illuminating treatise *Power Without Property*,[2] says that there is "no presently accepted theory of power," that we have neither a method nor the vocabulary permitting the comparison of power with anything else. In more scientific terms this means that power is not quantitatively describable. It seems to me that exactly this trait reveals its nature. Power, as was shown in Chapter 10, is rationalized animal instinct, and instinct has generally eluded quantitative analysis.

In a wider context, this inability to deal effectively with the concept of power signifies that man has never arrived at a corporate ethic. He had to remain content with calling those mechanisms through which power usually operates "pecking orders." You may hack your inferiors to death, but toward your superiors you are submissive, you bow and scrape and lick their boots. The inferior's attitude is determined by an automatic mechanism, while the superior is not bound by any code. In other words, complementarity is lacking; hence, according to our previous definition of ethic as complementarity risen to consciousness, the pecking order or power structure is per se unethical.

We here come face to face with a remarkable fact, which to my (limited) knowledge has been missed by all those who wrote on ethics *ex officio* as well as *en amateur*. To make this clear, we must go back to some points established in former chapters: (1) primitivity, as the first human stage above mere animalism, meant the supersedure of instinctual regulation of social relations by a conscious ethic, mixed, to be sure, with superstitious magic (which is probably a rudiment carried over into the human sphere from our animal existence, even if it goes under the name of revealed religion); (2) civilization, on the other hand, meant the superordination upon the primitive ethico-magical mentality of rational logic, at first no doubt very imperfect because, as rationalized instinct, it also has its subconscious element of magic.

Ethics, therefore, has always had reference to primitive social conditions, the small group or band within which everybody knows everybody. Murder within the group, for instance, became taboo, while the killing of outsiders was looked upon as a virtue—a state of things which to this day has survived in military affairs. In general, indeed, all human ethic has remained arrested on this primitive level. It has barely kept step with the growth of the primitive group into tribes and nations. Above all, it has, by and large, proved itself incapable of adapting to civilization, particularly those institutions typical of rational civilization: politics, commerce and industrial organization, with their hierarchies and power structures. So that, on the whole, all civilizations have suffered from the tragic situation that *ethics remained uncivilized and the institutions of civilization remained unethical.*

All systems of ethic, professional or amateur, invariably address themselves to primitive person-to-person relations, never, or extremely rarely, to the impersonal institutions of civilization. These, because of the distancing which abstract organization entails, still permit murder, predation and other severe damage to be perpetrated without the necessity of a face-to-face situation. Nowhere is this more strikingly apparent than in the indubitable fact that all through the history of civilization even ecclesiastical power structures ended up among the most immoral organizations. Official Christianity too discovered at an early date that "it pays" handsomely to preach individual morality and to reserve for "the system," that which civilized rationality superimposed on conditions of primitivity, "the higher right" to disregard its own preachings and as a body to behave unethically, criminally, albeit *ad maiorem Dei gloriam*. Conditions hardly changed when the monolithic power structure of the Roman Church was broken up by the Reformation. The systems of Luther, Calvin, Zwingli and other reformers revealed the same defects.

The fault is intrinsic in virtually all civilized organizations. In political literature, Thomas Hobbes has glorified the system in his *Leviathan*. As the one-eyed man has no proper perspective, Hobbes, with all his shrewd one-dimensional rationality, is absolutely devoid of ethic. His book reeks of thoroughgoing, if phosphorescent, putrefaction. And the situation has to this day remained typical of virtually all large corporate organizations. Bossism has remained the keynote of civilization, ours included. The great ethical problems of our day, those particularly which keep our world posed under a sword of Damocles, all arise, however, not from person-to-person relationships, but from the nature of our corporate establishments, secular and ecclesiastical, all equally unprincipled, and from the opportunity they provide individuals to vent their animal proclivities behind the façades, and through the medium of, impersonal organizations.

We have then, to repeat, arrived at the shocking conclusion that all ethic has remained primitively atavistic, whereas civilization in its one-sided rationality and its concentration on power has always been unethical. There has never been a specific ethic of civilization.[3] Not one of the major religions offers one. This is what made it so easy, indeed a delight, for a man to regard himself a paragon of a pious, God-fearing individual, so long as he obeyed the commands of primitive ethics (e.g., the Decalogue), because it still permitted him on the level of civilization, in business, politics, church administration, to behave without a qualm in such a way as to cause the starvation of thousands, their gradual death in squalor and physical exhaustion, while he himself grew fat and opulent. And the law, insofar as it did more than reformulate the thou-shalt-nots of primitive person-to-person relations, has until very recently been inclined to sanction civilized ways of predation, murder and other crimes, so long as they could be committed impersonally, institutionally, through the various power structures. But again it should be stressed that these are not class defects. Communist dictatorships offer clear evidence of this. The short-comings have so far been inherent in all civilizations and their dominant institutions, from feudalism, ecclesiastical and demo-cratic bossism down to educational institutions and labor unions. In all civilizations the essential complementarity of ethic and reason was short-circuited or somehow squashed. This has been the undoing of them all.

The life span of every living system, though, depends on its ethos, which means the specific way and the degree in which, and to which, fundamental complementarity has been embodied in the system. It may hence appear paradoxical that all civilizations succeeded in embodying the selfish instincts in elaborate institu-tions. But the paradox is spurious. Economic and defensive sys-tems are purely rational and mechanical affairs, and though they are social institutions, nominally benefiting all members of a group, even the most antisocial individuals have usually been willing to cooperate in their establishment. Indeed, they have not seldom proved "pioneers of progress," for the simple reason that the higher levels of material civilization always open up more lucrative fields of parasitic exploitation.[4]

However, to transform into a social force the sublimates of the reproductive instinct, altruism, self-transcending love, the highest forms of ethics, is quite another matter, beyond the power of organizing busybodies, secular or ecclesiastical. It cannot be done by "putting on the pressure," nor by any force of rational argumentation, because rationality to a large extent remains foreign to love. But precisely because, at heart, love is a most intimate matter it can become the touchstone of higher social evolution. Again, the paradox is not real. It is merely a way of saying that the highest levels of civilization can be reached only spontaneously, on the wave of full ethical maturity on the part of every individual, even in his corporate activities.

The problem, fundamentally, is common to all life and hence merely one which followed on the heels of man during his rise from the animal kingdom. Geneticists have not discovered yet how animal species manage to strike a balance between traits that are advantageous to the individual and those which are advantageous to the species. In fact, it seems that altruistic behavior among animals can benefit a population only where a majority behave altruistically. Man still faces the same dilemma insofar as altruism remains virtually restricted to the narrowest family. Nor does "philanthropy" provide the answer, it being little more than a euphemism and indirect confession of guilt, the sanctimonious return of part of the loot. If we dwell on this impasse, it is merely to point up its cruciality, with no pretense of any easy way out of the vicious circle of the selfish instincts. Nevertheless, seeing the problem is always the first step toward its solution.

This brings us to the all-important query, do we have any degree of control over our ethical maturing?

"FREE WILL"

The problem of "free will" has been the subject of learned quarrels for ages. The dispute is not yet settled, although, under the influence of the philosophy of the new physics, opinion seems to be leaning toward the recognition of volitional freedom. It is an issue that touches the heart of the ethical question as well as that of the question of freedom in general.

The term "free will" appears to me tautological. If there is will, it can only be free, and if it is not (relatively) free, it is not will.

A machine has no will but at best expresses some of the will of its maker and user. Wherefore the question of human will resolves itself into a question of whether man is a pure automaton or more than a mere machine.

On the one hand, it can hardly be denied that, insofar as mental functions are one with cerebral physiology, they are in part, at least, reflections of our heredity and to that extent predetermined. Man can only think *qua* man. However, as before indicated, hereditary determinacy is never more than hereditary routine, phylogenetic, ontogenetic or social. But routine fails in the face of every novel situation—it can only run to the end of beaten paths, no further. Hence, where it is absolute, evolution is out of the question. Here again it is to be remembered that on all levels evolution depends on the complementarity of routine and innovations—and innovations demand freedom. Routine then sees to it that novel acquisitions become permanent possessions. Furthermore, considering the astronomical number of links possible among brain cells, we may be sure that here, too, differences in degree become differences in kind. The thinking brain is more than an enlarged reflex center and thought is of an order beyond strict mechanism. Certainly original thought is.

But will itself is but a form of thought, like thought based in general on the perception of relations, and searching for means and ways to direct these relations toward a purpose. Will is thought in action, and unless we assume that all thought is rigidly predetermined, we must allow for the possibility that will cannot, or cannot wholly, be subject to causal laws.

The concept of freedom is today such an integral part of the new physics that some philosophers of science see no reason why a certain will should not be attributed even to the most elemental physical units. They see in all external reality "the putting itself forward of a will."[5] However that be, the human experience of arbitrary decisions, decisions not unequivocally implicit in a situation, is as indisputably part of an observed world order as any other empirically ascertained scientific fact.

Above all, however, the whole subject of ethics becomes stark hypothetical nonsense the moment we discard will. It can have no meaning except where men are free and responsible agents. And if we draw the last conclusion from the nature of complementarity, particularly the complementarity of reason and ethic, it is nothing less than this: denying ethic means denying reason as well, which is tantamount to an absolute negation of thought. Look at it as we will, there seems no alternative but either to accept the complementarity of reason and ethic, which is indeterminately non-mechanical thought and implies "free will," or to reject both reason and ethic. Complementarity, however, is the fount of all freedom as well as the negation of absolutism. As an aspect of the complementarity of reason and ethic, ethical will therefore must be free but, for the same cause, never absolutely and only conditionally free.

Until recently, physics, with its impressive array of mathematical formulae and admirable achievements, was in a position to impose its mechanistic-deterministic ways of thinking on all the mental disciplines, for it was taken as axiomatic that mathematics cannot be wrong. The classical physicist was not in a position to realize that he was drawing universal conclusions from limiting cases (somewhat like the savage who argued that, since possessions are good for men, thieving must be a virtue). Those, on the other hand, who were concerned with phenomena of life could bring into the battle of the wits only "common sense," which was not scientific according to the interpretation of "science" by those who used to have a monopoly on it. They could point out, though, with the biologist Driesch that absolute mental determinism entails its own negation. For if everything were predetermined in the monstrous clockwork of the universe, even errors and mistakes would be. So that mathematical "proofs" and experimental "demonstrations" would lose all validity, because in an absolute scheme everything is plain unarguable fact, and "right" and "wrong," "truth" and "untruth" become devoid of meaning.

In the social world, too, laws would be equally futile without the assumption of will and ethical responsibility. Here, too, the concepts of "right" and "wrong," without which no society could prevail, would become senseless superstitions. Still, the prestige of classical-deterministic physics was such that the taint of being unscientific lay heavily on all social disciplines. The deadlock between the two opposing schools remained long unbroken, with the result that, since "science" meant strict mechanism and life refused to demean itself to the mechanical level, political science remained a sort of alchemy, or, following the way of least resistance, it discarded the higher logic of life for the dead-end logic of political mechanism and the rigidly engineered state machine.

The advent of the new physics has changed the theoretical situation, if not the practical one. It must even be admitted that a valid theoretical construct has never been found to bridge the gap between the Heisenberg Indeterminacy and man's free will. Indeed, a "scientific proof" of any such connection may well be impossible. Logic, mathematical or other, is a deterministic mode of thought and hence not applicable to nondeterministic domains (hence the fallaciousness of all "proofs" of the existence of God). Nevertheless, since complementarity is as definitely part of the mental world of man as it is of microphysics, the inference is surely justified that there is an evolutionary (and hence irrational) connection between the merely negative indeterminacy of physics and the more positive (though never absolute) freedom of the mind, which is also a generally recognized empirical fact.

In complementarity is contained the unity of the world as well as its inexhaustible variety, the vital necessity of freedom as well as of integrative cooperation within an order of law. Life, then, has a meaning vaster and more serene than it ever had because, by recognizing freedom as an elemental part of the cosmic order, the furtherance of freedom became a desirable duty. In short, the new physics has disclosed to us as a central truth what the greatest thinkers of all ages have always intuitively grasped and taught as ethico-social gospel. Only because "in the beginning was freedom" could there be evolution. Freedom of will, as of thought, has become part of the universe of the new physics. In the words of Eddington, "That overweening phase, when it was almost necessary to ask permission of physics to call one's soul one's own, is past," and "science . . . withdraws its moral opposition to free-will."[6]

We are, then, again permitted to live in a free, that is, an ethical, world, as part of a universe which is the fruit of a determined past (and therefore a dead past), with deterministic factors such as heredity, tradition, and other fairly strict directives reaching out of the past. On the other hand, the present is the germ of a future at least partly free, in whose shaping we must take a hand to justify our claim to be alive and fully human.

The laws we adopt are such attempts, but laws are only the lowest common denominators of individual behavior and of the social ethos. Above the formal law, life still depends on an infinity of individual decisions which no law is in a position to influence. This is our freedom, the judicious use of which may be conducive to even larger freedom, whereas its abuse can mean only the ultimate loss of freedom. The use or misuse of freedom, that is the province of ethics, and ethics therefore, as Aristotle and the ancient Chinese knew, is the very crux of politics.

Unfortunately, it is still axiomatic that, like oil and water, politics and ethics "won't mix." This is the tragic side of our own civilization as it has been of all others. The much vaunted argument, that technology has made our globe too small for anything but world government, is plainly childish. For the truth is that human ethic, especially political and economic ethic, has remained too rudimentary for this shrunken world, too often even for a small nation-state. We behold the promised land of a united world, but are barred from it because of ethical disqualification. We still refuse to see that narrowing elbow room demands a larger ethic, though we have realized to our cost that shrinking ethic always clamors for more *Lebensraum*.

Now what of the freedom of the will with regard to this question? Are we really free to will, and to work for, that ethic which is the prerequisite for better government and government on a larger scope?

We know that our freedom is not absolute, but sharply curtailed. No man can have more freedom than he is born with, or born to, because he is bound to an organic system, the constitution of which he cannot transgress. However, there is still the chance that the organically given potentialities can in some measure be developed. For man is not purely the product of biological heredity. He is as much, or even more, the fruit of the environment in which he is raised.

The great uncertainty is chiefly to what extent under favorable circumstances constructive will can be fostered, and in what direction, toward what aims, it can be encouraged to work. Freedom in general, though limited, can no longer be questioned. All evolution bears witness to this, even if it may have been largely the freedom of contingencies. Equally certain it is that at all times firm law and order must form a major part of life and constitute a complex of deterministic factors, meaning the lack of certain freedoms. On the other hand, whatever order there is in man's world has resulted from the free exercise of choice, from the voluntary renunciation of certain freedoms so that we may the better develop those holding out the promise of more worthwhile forms of order embodying still greater freedom. Even freedom, including that of volition, makes sense only within the law, as the law makes sense only within an order of freedom. Social orders are neither strictly the result of evolutionary contingencies nor of evolutionary mechanisms, but always represent to a considerable degree what men have freely chosen. The various cultures and civilizations therefore are still within the laws of nature, representing, as they do, merely a complex of selections from all the possibilities within the cosmic order. In this sense, law, too, denotes free choice, and the wise law will lead to ever more precious freedom.

This may sound like an elaborate abstraction. There is, though, one sphere of modern life which answers in no uncertain terms the question, to what extent can man transform the world when volition and strict ethic team together?

That domain is science.

THE QUEST OF TRUTH

Like ethic, science is in part the gift of society. To make this clear, let us assume that Isaac Newton had been born one of identical twins, and that this hypothetical twin of his—Abraham—had been carried off into the New England wilderness. Abraham Newton, though potentially the same great genius as Isaac, would never have left his mark on science. The Puritan environment of early New England would have suppressed his genius, as the milieu of the Old World brought out that of Isaac. Where there is science and ethic, at least half of the merit is always that of society as a whole because neither can flourish where social selection decides against them, where they are not *appreciated*.

What is significant here is that *appreciation*, the recognition of the preciousness of certain facts, is nothing but one of the many transfigured forms of love. True science is a form of respect and veneration shown objects, data and truths as entities in their own right, irrespective of whether they can satisfy an animal craving or not; and being a transmuted form of love, it is also a form of self-sacrifice to the benefit of all. The crass egoist will never be a man of science. Pure science is the love of truth. As such it is as much a manifestation of the highest ethic as of pure reason. In this one field of human endeavor, the marriage of ethic and reason is celebrating supreme triumphs over the animal in man.

The antonyms of science are charlatanism, deceit, quackery, commercialism, any kind of trickery that *pays*, whereas the true scientist, like the true artist, the saint and prophet, will often starve and suffer rather than be unfaithful to his principles. It is absolutely out of question to achieve scientific results and scientific stature by such unethical means as have often perverted political life, and even the quest of God, into plain rackets. Pure science therefore gives us a most encouraging answer to our question, whether man is free to will to work for the love of the highest ethic. Once a few leaders have shown the way, others may follow and establish a tradition, an environment favorable to the pursuit of truth. Since man is endowed with reason to indemnify him for what he lost in instinctive surety, he can be environmentally encouraged to choose a better way of life than that of base animal desires.

The contention that science is the *only* aspect of civilization inherently ethical demands still more careful consideration in order not to appear a piece of dogmatism. Contrary to purely intellectual achievements, ethic is shared by most, or all. It expresses the empirical wisdom of our ancestors that society stands or falls with the conversion, or nonconversion, of animal behavior into considered conduct, the taking into account of the community. Ethic thus becomes the trustee within the individual of the concerns of all, the guardian of truths more universal than the necessarily limited truths pertaining only to the individual. Governing the relations of all to all, it is, so to speak, a diffuse sort of prescientific social science, formulating these relations as best it can with the means available.

This ethical basis is also one of the germs of science, which, having grown far beyond it, now aims at nothing less than the impartial investigation of the relations of all things to all things. In brief, its purpose is truth, which is an ethical as well as a rational value. Regardless of the immense rational diversification in specialized science, its common ethical foundation remains. Science, too, stands or falls with its ethic, and reason is merely the dynamic scouting partner in this unequaled marriage of harmonious opposites. No other field of life reveals so clearly the creative nature of true complementarity and the freedom that is its reward. All this explains why it is as scientific, not as Christian, that our civilization may honestly be called the greatest. It is Western science, not religion, that has commanded the respect of the entire world. Only since the rise of modern science have a great many been permitted to choose the difficult pursuit of truth, which religious dogmatism never tolerated. For this reason alone, and in this domain of life alone, has Western civilization far outdistanced all older ones. Only an ethic without peer could bear fruit without precedent.

It is this ethic, too, which makes today's world of pure science "one world," whereas in every other province our planet still presents the old beastly struggle, in which instinct is pitted against instinct, greed against greed, class against class, dogma against dogma, and superstition against superstition. In the field of pure science alone do we already behold the world united and living in peaceful cooperation. Peace too is the fruit of ethics and of ethics alone.

Our age in its most characteristic aspects is an age of science. And though we are still at the very beginning of scientific development, already it is evident that, if science were eliminated, Western civilization would lose all face. But for exactly this reason the fate of our civilization would seem to depend on the ability, or failure, of a majority of us to make the standards of science our own. In blunt terms, to accept the material benefits of science, while rejecting the ethic implicit in it, is plain depravity and bound forever to breed corruption. We have the choice to accept or refute the situation, all or nothing, but we cannot with impunity enjoy only its facile sides, or what promises profits, and for the rest, in the manner made famous by certain politicians, ecclesiastics, and even some "humanists," sneer at the scientific mind. Again, it is immoral. No halfway measure is possible, except coupled to ruinous conflict and decadence.

Even where one might expect the evolutionary significance of science to be understood, the fact that it is the union of the keenest reason with the highest ethic is seldom grasped, or is suppressed as too disturbing. Certainly the ethical side of science is never reflected in the daily press, nor in the shouting from the pulpits. And with few exceptions, science, especially in the lower schools, is taught with a poverty of spirit as disheartening as that of the common trades, particularly under the increasing bias of political and commercial subsidies. The marriage of reason and ethic, which alone can give science its evolutionary impetus, is thus systematically undermined by designing powers, with the result that science is already in danger of coming to rest, not on a basis of objectivity, but on a foundation of bribes with their attendant evil of prejudice and the diversion from the pursuit of truth to fawning before vested interests. But where science is still unfettered, has it not given proof that it can open the way to a greater and richer world beyond the barriers of the selfish instincts?

Whether our civilization as a whole may enter the promised land will depend above all on whether politics and economics, the chief public instinct fields, and their technological henchmen are able to rise to the level of the ethic of science. Every other hope held out to us is open to suspicion. In this light, one of the more controversial of Plato's sayings assumes new importance:

> Until philosophers are kings, or the kings and princes of this world have the spirit and power of philosophy, and political greatness and wisdom meet in one, and those commoner natures who pursue either to the exclusion of the other are compelled to stand aside, states will never have rest from their evils—no, nor the human race, as I believe—and then only will this our state have a possibility of life and behold the light of day.[7]

Pettifoggers of all hues have always done their best to ridicule these words by the cheap trick of holding up to us the image of a sallow little campus philosopher garbed in rented purple. They have always carefully ignored the fact that in Plato's time philosophy meant science as much as it meant anything. His philosopher-king, therefore, is a genius in statesmanship, in political science and political philosophy in one, a man who can make creative use in politics of that one great trait which alone makes man more than an animal—*vision*, the kind of vision that perceives the relations among things and can direct them to fruitful ends. This, surely, is the test of great statesmanship as well as of science and philosophy;

and the man who lacks such vision can be neither a good statesman, nor a scientist or philosopher.

Yet the remarkable thing is that even a historian of the stature of Toynbee[8] made every effort to confuse the issue between Plato's philosopher and king in order to arrive at the prejudiced conclusion that, as far as modern civilization is concerned, our only hope lies in a return to the mother church. To Toynbee (though in later writings he somewhat softened his protest) science is a treasonable movement, and he resents the fact that it has shifted "the rising edifice of our Western Civilization from a religious to a secular basis." I prefer the less biased evolutionary view that it would be as disastrous for any civilization, as it would be for the individual, to "enter the second time into his mother's womb." All evolution, being time become manifest, is a directional and irreversible process. A scientifically justified *Weltanschauung*, that is, an outlook based on universal *vision* and embodying the deepest love of objective truth, could not without cataclysmic results be reconverted into—figuratively speaking—the diffuse *Weltbeschnüffelung*, or global *olfaction*, which was its evolutionary starting point.

Toynbee's view is based on the assumption of the irreconcilability of science and religion, which arises from a severe lack of evolutionary insight. In fact, the two represent the outcome of self-differentiation in a once unitary field of thought and as such remain to a large extent each other's complement. I shall have more to say on this topic at the end of this chapter, but here I want to emphasize that if throughout this discussion I have taken a somewhat idealized view of science, this was in no way prompted by a desire to deify it. The science I have been speaking of is, after all, still a very tenuous current. To the majority of the scientifically trained, science still has no meaning other than the promise of better jobs. They are technicians and specialists only, differing from ordinary mechanics only insofar as, instead of union cards, they hold sheepskins. As far as this class of "scientists" is concerned, there is no doubt more than a grain of truth in the contention that secular knowledge is at the root of the world's evils. But the reproach does not touch pure science. Nor can it be too often repeated that the main shortcomings of our civilization are not those of science itself, but those of an unscientific dominant class motivated by overt or covert animal instincts.

Nor can it be denied that applied science itself does contain the possibility of becoming man's undoing if it forgets that science is a "gift of society." It cannot, therefore, be a purpose in itself, but must ever be aware of its obligation to take its main orientation from society as a whole. It can have no absolute freedom. The atomic situation of today should make this obvious. Complete freedom for the nuclear scientists could not but mean the complete self-defeat of science, because it would mean the end of all life on earth. The same is true of chemical technology which, to judge by the intensifying pollution of the world's waters, air, soil and foods, shows every indication of pressing toward a chemists' Walpurgis Night. Surely the casuistry with which some specialists in these fields try to hide the facts from themselves is hardly worthy of the name of science.

Again, therefore, science can benefit mankind only if it remains oriented toward society and the total structure of life supporting it. Science is, after all, something that exists only in the minds of men and became possible only through a long social tradition.

This brings us back once more to the question of religion and the general spiritual impact of science on modern society. As has often been pointed out by others, Copernicus removed man from the center of the universe which theological fiction (using the term in its most exalted sense) once had granted him. And Darwin dealt medieval man the final *coup de grâce* by denying him the status of God's own very special pet and reducing him to just one among a million other creatures of evolution. Now it cannot be denied that this advance of scientific "truth" upon theological "fiction" (also called "truth") has left us the heritage of a void which nothing has so far been able to fill. Only the callous have escaped the shock; all the rest, consciously or unconsciously, suffer from its traumas, as the general unrest of our age demonstrates. Science itself alone can probably never hope to fill that void. It has its own purposefully circumscribed and maintained limits, beyond which everything becomes (often in a disparaging sense) "metaphysics." Yet I would not hold the situation hopeless. Even scientists know that, as George Sarton said, "We cannot live on truth alone." Some of the theoretical physicists, Schrödinger[9] for instance, move in some of their writings in spheres hard to distinguish from the religious. E. W. Sinnott,[10] a phytogeneticist, has repeatedly emphasized that science and religion are only different aspects of the human mind. Some scientists find spiritual compensation in beauty, be it the "elegance" of their (or others') equations, the fascination of a landscape, of a flower, or of the starry firmament. Indeed, the beauty of modern mathematico-physical abstractions itself has been likened to pure abstract art, satisfying something that transcends the intellect.

These are, I think, auspicious signs. As we have said before, life in its very essence is self-transcendence, which ultimately is an expression of fundamental complementarity. But, and this needs emphasizing, it is of the very nature of complementarity that its various aspects must harmonize. Evolutionary change in one calls for a corresponding change in the other. The main "transcendental" aspect of human life has up to now been presented by religion. Traditional religions, however, without exception antedate modern science and as presumable absolutes and "eternal verities" have not changed. They are thus "off-key" in an age of science or, if a crude simile be permitted, as anomalous as the heart of a fish in the body of man.

Now, religions cannot be created arbitrarily. They are as much psycho-organic manifestations of certain developmental stages as are other aspects of human life. We may profitably remind ourselves here that the era of the Great Mother, the universal goddess of mammalian-matronal primitivity, came to an end when the males of the species rose to dominance in civilizations, and that the men conceived their supreme deities in their own image. None of these has enjoyed eternal life either. Even Yahweh, the blustering, thundering, irascible and intolerant god of the early Jews has survived in name only. I hold it not impossible that an age of science, once it has reached mental maturity (ours is still in its adolescent phase) will give rise to its own transcendental lore (though we of this age might hesitate to call it religion) in harmony with its own ethico-rational concepts. In the words of John Donne: "Reason is our soul's left hand, faith her right. By these we reach divinity."

Traditionalists may sneer at this as blasphemy and ironclad rationalists as mysticism. While we let the former stew in their self-righteous indignation, we may ask the latter two questions: why is it that a light ray of wave length 5×10^{-7} appears green to us? and, what is the physical nature of a physicist's thoughts? Until science can answer these questions (some scientists admit that they will remain unanswerable), it is hard to see how a certain transcendentalism can be kept out of human life. Color, thought and related phenomena have no place in quantitative science, but are all-important to human consciousness. As one physicist put it, "Man, regarded quantitatively, consists of very interesting chemical substances possessing even more interesting functions and reactions—but then he is no longer a man."[11] Quantitative science is an adventure in lowest common denominators. And these largely disqualify in evolutionary considerations.

But to come back now to the possibility of a new spiritual life in agreement with a mature science, I would like to illustrate what I mean by using the example of music as an analogy. Of all our arts music is the most abstract, the one most purely "technical," so much so that the greatest works could be transposed into strictly mathematico-physical symbols without losing any of their values. Radio and the phonograph prove that purely mechanical renditions sacrifice barely a trace of music's "otherworldliness." None of the other, less purely technical, arts ever achieves the height of spiritual exultation, the cosmic grandeur, the divinity and religious fervor which "purely technical" music attains at the hands

of the masters. This seems to me of tremendous heuristic significance. Conceivably, then, a new spiritual life of civilization
(whether we call it religion or philosophy, or by some other name,
seems of little importance) akin to the spirit of great music may
some day emerge from the abstractions and technicalities of science. At present we are merely "fiddling" with technical ideas. The
scientific "symphonies" remain a hope. A prime condition for their
realization would seem to be that scientists themselves burst their
journeymen's chrysalis and become aware that even in their minut-
est technical details they are dealing with aspects of cosmic evolution, in which man has become a participant and is no longer a
mere on-looker. What of it if he is no longer the center of the
universe? The present (Einsteinian) universe has no center.

The static-finalistic world view of the Middle Ages is no longer
tenable. Evolution is by all indications continuing. We ourselves
are only temporary end products of it and still in the mainstream
of evolutionary change. If we can gather any wisdom from this
scientific insight, we may to some extent direct our own evolution.
Then the great void around us may someday again become replete
with meaning. Another very important condition of our future
evolution would seem to be that even politics become pervaded
by, or converted to, the new spirit of science, its objectivity, its
ethics and visionariness, its endeavor to remain attuned to cosmic
"truths" as they gradually become revealed to its untiring search.
So far in history politics has always proved an evolutionary bottle-
neck, if not a deadly trap.

17

REVIEW AND EPILOGUE

WE have come to the end of a journey which to some may have seemed rather incredible and hence is promptly to be dismissed from the mind. The notion of fundamental law, especially in so far as it might affect human conduct, is still distasteful to many. Though they may concede its place in physics, they prefer to derive from man's animal ancestors "the sacred human right" to do as they please. It may therefore not be inappropriate to begin this summary by quoting an eminent mathematical physicist, a sharp mind not always free of cynicism, P. W. Bridgman:

> To a number of persons the Heisenberg principle of indetermination [or Bohr's complementarity] has seemed evidence of something with deeper significance than a purely mathematical non-commutability of p and q numbers. One would like to find out how to handle this new principle intuitively, in its own right, divorced from the severe mathematical considerations that gave rise to it. . . . I think such attempts should be judged sympathetically, as experiments in thinking which may be enormously fruitful, instead of harshly from the narrow point of view of the special mathematical theory which happened to give the first suggestion.[1]

This passage came to my attention only during a revision of this last chapter and was not a starting point. But it does sum up what seized my mind when I came upon Bohr's complementarity: to "handle this new principle . . . in its own right," as something that promised to be "enormously fruitful."

As indicated in the introductory chapter, Bohr himself (the son of a physiologist) by suggestion, at least, extended the principle from pure physics to physiology and the human psyche. We have found reason to deem it valid even in human society, to appreciate it as the primary principle of organization and the evolutionary principle par excellence.

In its simplest form it is the determinant of the main architectural features of the inert and the living world. This is apparent in the inseparableness of such conjugate and asymmetrical pairs as space and time, the material and wave nature of microphysical particles, the positively charged proton and the negative electron, the atomic nucleus and the electronic mantle, the nucleus and cytoplasm of the living cell, the interdependence of organism and environment, the sexual dimorphism of most living species; the division of life into a vegetable and an animal kingdom, and of the highest levels of human organization into a social realm proper and a political realm. There is a related division even in the sphere of the individual mind: on the one hand the subconscious and the conscious realm, and within the latter the complementarity of ethics and reason.[2] From space and time up to ethics and reason, the bond within the pairs is "organic," not mechanical. A mechanical principle would have permitted no evolution. Nor can we any longer harbor serious doubts that human civilizations represent the highest evolutionary developments on this foundation.

It is often said that man and his works are the product of a fortuitous and purposeless natural process, not of any planning. At first sight, especially in view of the millions of evolutionary casualties, this opinion seems fairly convincing. Recently, however, some evolutionists, and even physicists, have urged a modification. We have already mentioned it: "Chance has no meaning except in a setting of order."[3] Without using the term "complementarity" its essence is thus introduced as basic to world structure and evolution.

The conjugateness of chance and order is especially evident in
genetic mutations and natural selection. Mutations "out of order"
are ruthlessly eliminated.

The basic order, still allowing almost unlimited scope for chance,
evidently is the complementarity of the living system and the environment. This of course still leaves many philosophical problems
unanswered. Even if man seems to have adhered more persistently
than any other creature to the one principle which alone can
vouchsafe continuous evolution, the question of purpose or plan
is, after all, merely transferred from his own origin to that of the
purposefulness or fortuity of the primal principle and hence is
more than reason can confidently answer in the affirmative or the
negative. Practically, it seems to matter little which way men
choose to answer the Ultimate Question. In fact, since the be-
lievers in planned creation have generally proved capable of behaving as abominably as the unbelievers, one may sympathize
with those who, disavowing planned abomination, devoutly side
with the unbelievers.

However, if the answer to the Ultimate Question remains a
predilection of faith, the fact of the primary principle's rising to
consciousness in human ethics, the awareness that we are all part
of each other, disqualifies mere faith as a yardstick of human
integrity. What becomes decisive is conduct deriving its norms
from the indisputable truth that individual and species (or society)
are complementary aspects of one phenomenon. Thus, contrary
to most of what has been said on this subject, there is after all a
natural basis for ethic. But it is a mistake to look for it on the
animalic-organic level. That basis lies much deeper. It is identical
with the fundamental organizational principle of the world, complementarity, as every kind of organization implicitly contains, if
not an ethic, at least an ethos. Nevertheless, even if we discover
ethics to have a universal basis, its manifestations are determined
by evolutionary processes and hence are always specific, i.e., vari-
able, depending on numerous factors of a hereditary as well as of
a cultural (environmental) nature. There can be no single, abso-

lute and eternally valid ethics, and those who deny it are likely sooner or later to become the species' ethical laggards. The current religious controversy over birth control may serve as an illustration.

All of which of course means that even a social and political order is "the work of nature," that hence it can persist only as long as it keeps within nature's fundamental laws. Man may be unique, but that does not give him the right to equate uniqueness with unnaturalness. The oft-defended view that advanced civilizations lie outside the pale of nature is beginning to look like the last shabby vestige of the old anthropocentric superstition.

Political civilization, we saw, has a genetic foundation and is *species integration* on the highest evolutionary level. It is based on the complementarity of individual and state, of groups and the state, as well as, in the long view, of all states and the species. Thereby are defined the natural and foremost political tasks: the exercise of all functions conducive to the universality of the species-state, or, until we have the latter, the guardianship against the deterioration of political life from a close-to-universal scope to any of the countless possible limiting cases. Politics can remain a positive evolutionary factor only as long as it operates within the world's basic principle. If we could succeed in making this scientific perspective prevail, the results would be beyond all expectations.

To single out but one aspect from among a thousand: the vital *problem of peace*, on which just now hinges our survival as a civilization. The principle of complementarity alone, if properly and generally understood, can provide an enduring foundation for peace among men, within and between nations. Not merely a basis for the abolition of war, but for fruitful cooperation between all individuals, all groups, nations, continents, races. It would lead infinitely further than anything ever proposed as a foundation for peace. For it is of the very essence of the involved mystery of the world's primal cause, that which makes it the evolutionary principle par excellence, that it always means oneness in multiplicity and multiplicity in unity. *It requires diversity yet makes for vital unity.* You simply cannot organize equals, except mechanically, and mechanism is, we saw, a limiting case of "cosmic fundamentalism." You cannot integrate equals, only add them, and addition is a deadly operation. Life on the other hand, from the "living crystals" up, has always been complementary diversity, and evolution never anything but greater and greater diversification within a whole. No politico-economic creed, no religious dogma has ever offered such potentialities; on the contrary, they have always been among the foremost causes of war.

In every state there is of course much to be achieved before we even have the moral right to hope for a more peaceful world. The problem here is that posed by the authority of the state and the freedom of the individual. Generally, the solutions suggested have been in the nature of compromises. Compromise represents about the limit of intellectual understanding to which politics has progressed, but from the evolutionary viewpoint it is about as inane as speaking of marriage as a compromise between the extremes of perversion. The political perversion, common to dictatorships and democracies, lies in seeing the state as a collective of individuals.[4] It draws all its conclusions from a static cross section and neglects the depth of time which alone can reveal the state to be a process of complementary special integration, in which process neither the state nor the individual has any absolute meaning. As absolutes both are unreal abstractions.

As an ideal, complementarity as the decisive principle of the state has of course long been vaguely anticipated. But the ideal has never been remotely approached. In practice, through all recorded history, politics, in its secular as in its ecclesiastical variety, has never been anything but the glorification of power. But power, as the rationalization of predatory animal instincts, has always proved a treacherous atavism and self-defeating. Power must, to be sure, be given credit for conjuring civilization out of the primeval vegetative-mammalian order. But for this very reason it remains, so to speak, the "original sin" of civilization and can for the same reason perhaps never be quite dispensed with. However, like another "original sin," it too remains a "sin" only so long as it is unalleviated by the piety which was its evolutionary precursor as the dominant organizer of primitivity: the ethic of brotherly and filial love.

A great deal has been said in this book on the subject of love, and others keep saying more about it. The caveat is, therefore, in order that love alone, or mutual respect, altruism, humaneness, or whatever we choose to call it, is not enough. Because from the very beginning evolution has been the evolution of *organization*. It is organization alone which distinguishes living from lifeless phenomena, and vital, "creative," evolution has always proceeded on the principle which has been our central theme. Perhaps this is still hard to grasp. Among the most recent exegetes of love not even Teilhard de Chardin understood this. His poetic, visionary epic of man[5] remains, therefore, in part at least, misleading mysticism founded on faulty science. Even in his supreme concept, his eschatological "Point Omega," he too remains arrested in mere collectivism, *additivité dirigée*. This is the old disastrous theological view of mankind as a living sand pile blown by the winds of heaven. To some degree this also applies to the Jesuit Father's Protestant counterpart, Albert Schweitzer.

Mere mysticism too represents a dead end, because it is the absolute negation of organization, a form of philosophical anarchism. Religion has proved itself as impotent a peacemaker as crass materialism.

It must therefore be stressed again and again that civilization means species integration, and integration means *organization* on the basis of the primal principle. Now love is, to be sure, a form of complementarity, the most intense experience of it in man's existence. By its very nature, however, it remains, at least in its commonly accepted sense, a primitive (because partly physiological) social microcosm whose emanations are apt to fade in geometrical proportion with distance. Poets may sing of love ignited by a windborne hair. Most of us, though, cannot truly love people we do not know and have never seen. Civilization demands something that can unite all as love unites two. This something is ethic. It is the offspring of love evoked by reason. Love is unreasonable because irrational. Ethic, if still far from pure rationality, is much more reasonable. And while it too has its origin on the primitive level and dominates primitive societies, it is, because of its rational component, extensible to the macroscopic scale of civilization. Being both love and reason, it makes possible *organization* in virtually unlimited dimensions. Nothing is therefore so fallacious as Albert Schweitzer's dictum that ethic "can no longer be founded on, and justified by, a [mere] *Weltanschauung.*" The very contrary is the case. Ethic is implicit in, an integral part of, the world view now beginning to emerge from the theory of complementarity.

Because ethic is part and parcel of the new scientific world view, it offers, in my opinion, the one and only possibility for peace among men: organized ethic or ethical organization. Neither ethic alone nor organization alone will get us very far. Here, again, evolution depends on complementarity. Except in the earliest phases of civilizations the ethic of religion never had any bearing on political organization and politics no bearing on religion. Ethic can unite the fruitful qualities of both. Moreover, all religions have proved ephemeral. They come and go, and such of them as last too long invariably become as atavistic as pets in a human household. Ethic is less tied to temporal, local and ethnic circumstances than are the religions. Its roots reach into a deeper, more fundamental evolutionary stratum and its terrestrial horizons (which is what counts here) are vaster than those of religion. Hence it can be both more eternal and more universal than religion. And, once again, let us not forget this, ethic has recently become a scientific value. In a presumptively "scientific" civilization we ought to be able to muster enough integrity to draw the consequences from this truth. It is the only foundation on which world peace can become possible.

This still leaves us with the problem of how to achieve a civilization founded on ethic. Certainly, it will be a slow process, and for this reason everything that prevents the global thermonuclear holocaust must be supported. This much, at least, may be said here: contrary to love, which is wholly irrational, ethic, having a rational element, can to some extent be taught. The problem hence is one of education as well as of law. It would demand a certain de-emphasis of purely technical *training* on all levels of education and a renascence of humanistic *education,* in the old-fashioned sense but in a new spirit. Today, practically all schools are trade schools, schools for mechanics. The social mechanism is their ultimate concept and accounts for the perennial cropping up of such panaceas of despair as orthodox socialism, Communism, the various fascist dictatorships, and even Lyndon B. Johnson's Great Society. All are simplistic lucubrations, adolescent in character, because born of naïve mechanism.

Mechanism is a dead end because it is an epigonous, secondary, phenomenon in cosmic evolution. All primary phenomena are "organic" in the sense in which the world's fundamental principle is organic. Mechanism can be a valuable aid, a priceless servant in evolution, as indeed no organism, no society, can do without it. But it cannot be the master, because the organic level represents the quintessence and the "meaning" of life and evolution.

The speculations on the meaning of life are numerous. From the point of view developed in these pages one can say only that the meaning of life and evolution rests in the fact that as "organic" events they are contrary to pure mechanism and that as manifestations of fundamental complementarity their essence is self-transcendence. To me that seems enough. It is left to everyone to interpret this according to his personal inclination, either sociologically, psychologically or religiously. In every special domain the self-transcendence of life is simply an aspect of the organism-environment complementarity. That, of course, makes the solipsist, the "rugged individualist," a complete humbug, but there is no help for it. Modern psychiatrists know to what formerly unsuspected extent self-transcendence is identical with self-realization and that its absence is pathological.

Concerning the bearing of the results of our inquiry on our

future political development, I would not deem it impossible at least to formulate a program based on evolutionary fundamentals. Its aim would be better local and national government and also government on a larger scale, embodying temporary and rough approximations to the distant ideal of species integration on a global scale. This should not sound too dogmatic, since, after all, sober and realistic "democratic" principles to some extent already embody some of the ideals we found to be in accord with natural law. The theoretical side of such a task might well be formulated satisfactorily within a generation or two, provided it were entrusted to the most farseeing, the most objective sociological, legal, scientific and psychological talent available, and not to the spokesmen of vested interests.

Regarding the practical realization of an ideal blueprint for a harmonious world, one is bound to maintain a more skeptical attitude, and for rather paradoxical reasons. The greatest resistance to be overcome would probably not be that of the material vested interests, but ethico-religious concepts which have also crystallized into power structures. There would be legal ways of dealing with the first but none to deal with the second. One could almost count on these latter to sabotage the most mature proposals. For these could hardly be of much practical value without offering at least tentative solutions of such fundamental questions as eugenics, population control, perhaps even the redistribution of populations and races with a view toward what we called "mental speciation" (I do not consider cultural uniformity desirable even in a united world). Some of these problems in all parts of the world are inseparable from concepts believed to be immutable and eternal verities.

In short, almost everywhere any scientifically and ethically mature plan would rouse the anger of groups living in the pride of fulfilling the staunchest and highest moral codes. Ethical absolutism would stake us down where we are today. One can argue with reason to make it see the necessity of ethics, but it can be extremely difficult to make absolute ethics perceive the need for reason. This is the drawback of its being the vegetative-static side of human mentality, and the explanation, why an absolute moral code in time can, and often does, become immoral in an evolving world.

We have seen that if there is one absolute and universal principle, it is complementarity alone, which by definition rules out absolutism. Thus, ethics emerges as probably the greatest of all our problems, being as disastrous where it is lacking as where it is fossilized. Evolutionary possibilities and evolutionary freedom, however, can arise only from the "marriage" of reason and ethic. So far, unfortunately, neither secular nor religious education is doing much, if anything, to achieve this end.

This brings us back once more to science as presently the most perfect "marriage" of reason and ethics. Since it is going to play an increasingly vital role in our lives, it will be increasingly necessary even for those active in other fields at least to understand its philosophical aspects and not merely to accept unthinkingly the marketable goods it produces. The more crucial science becomes as a revolutionary force, the more it imposes on us the obligation to emulate the unparalleled "marriage" of reason and ethics in the social or political world. Unless we morally merit the gifts of science, it will be our fate to perish by them. This, of course, applies also to the social behavior of scientists themselves. Scientific ethics as a merely intramural and socially irrelevant affair is bound to remain sterile. We therefore need an entirely new breed of scientific specialists, men who can view even minor problems within the whole of life, for only to the extent that they can do so are they truly scientists and not merely specialists and technicians. But we also need a new breed of scholars: sociologists, jurists, economists, political scientists, psychologists, philosophers, and even theologians familiar with the facts of life and evolution. Only if all scientific and scholarly activities and the knowledge they bring to light become integrated and related to "cosmic fundamentalism" (in the sense in which we have introduced this term) can they lead to what has long been held to be the highest aim of human striving: wisdom.

Here all civilizations have foundered and we ourselves are poised on the verge of failure. Our extensive scientific and scholarly knowledge has brought us no wisdom. Certainly narrow specialism has not, though we find encouraging signs of striving for it among some outstanding biologists and atomic physicists, men to whom science is inseparable from philosophy and who are imbued with the certainty of the dependence of all life on its evolutionary substructure, terrestrial as well as cosmic. Nor can wisdom, strictly, be considered an individual achievement. I know of no truly wise individuals, living or historical. On the other hand—very, very rarely—wisdom is met with within the confines of an exceptional family, even among a few primitive societies. It is, therefore, a fruit of social conditions, always integrally compounded of ethics (or love) and an appropriate measure of intelligence. But a wise civilization the world has never known, the reason being that a surfeit of intelligence unwedded to love or ethic is but a glorified form of self-defeating incompetence, smart obscurantism. A good deal of our specialism in all walks of life is just that.

Nothing expresses all this so well as our maxim "Time is Money." Time shrinks to a moment yielding a coin, a particle of solidified space to hold on to. The marriage of space and time dissolves, and this in turn entails a forfeiture of freedom, since there is freedom only in the basic principle. We live in a spiritual muddle, a world of unrelated thought. Hence freedom of enterprise has made more slaves than the world ever knew. Freedom of communication has added its quota through the film, radio, television and the popular press. And freedom of religion is to a large extent the freedom to refuse to grow up and, therefore, in some instances, even the freedom of a sort of sanctified juvenile delinquency. Freedom, though, is above all the freedom of evolution. And evolution, biological and social, is a matter primarily concerning the species or population. This would seem to be the point from which to start rethinking our crucial problems if our civilization is not to join the ranks of those which never survived their infancy.

Government could help, but not as long as, schizophrenically, half of its mind dotes on seventeenth- and eighteenth-century notions and the other half is given to the idolatry of gadgets and power. Still, I cannot, as others have done, advocate the curtailment of government on the pretext, for example, that it would promote human happiness. More government of the kind we have assuredly is undesirable, more of a better kind would no doubt constitute a gain. The pursuit of happiness itself, though, is suspect. If we lack happiness it is as much owing to our inability to provide better government than to anything else. We have the governments we deserve. Besides, happiness in the popular sense is probably more an infantile harking back rather than an ideal to be taken very seriously. Based as it is on purely individual sensation, it has little social, and hence evolutionary, value and as a steady diet is as demoralizing as a regimen of candy and cocktails. However, it will retain its rightful place in the nursery and the family.

By contrast, I cannot think of a single great achievement in the arts, in philosophy or science which is the fruit of the pursuit of happiness. What pleasure such works may provide is incidental, for the men who created them set their sights higher. We should learn to do the same in politics, and it might not be amiss in this connection to remember that man himself is incidental to the earth, the solar system, the Milky Way, the universe. Nobody could have brought him forth apart from the cosmic background. We did not get where we are on a shortcut.

Notes
and
References

INTRODUCTION

1. A. Heusler, *Institutionen des deutschen Privatrechts* (Leipzig, 1885), Intro.

2. On this topic, see F. Kern, *Kingship and the Law in the Middle Ages*, trans. by S. B. Chrimes (Oxford, Blackwell, 1939).

3. Cf., e.g., M. Planck, *A Survey of Physical Theory* (1920; New York, Dover, 1960) p. 1: "As long as Natural Philosophy exists, its ultimate aim will always be the correlating of various physical observations into a unified system, and, where possible, into a single formula." Further on he defines the aim of science as "the unity of the picture [of the world], unity of all separate parts of the picture, unity of space and time, unity of all experimenters, nations, cultures."

4. Some readers may find that in the following the term "complementarity" has been used to excess. I would therefore emphasize with Kant that in the interest of clarity it is not advisable to use too many synonyms for a well-defined technical term, "because it might easily happen that . . . even the idea gets lost which that word alone could have preserved." *Kritik der reinen Vernunft*, Hartenstein ed., p. 257; for Bohr's ideas on the subject of complementarity, see his collected essays, *Atomic Physics and Human Knowledge* (New York, Wiley, 1958).

5. D. Schindler and J. J. Kindt-Kiefer. See Notes 6, 7, Chpt. 13.

279

CHAPTER 1

1. See, e.g., M. Born, *The Restless Universe* (1936; New York, Dover, 1951); L. de Broglie, *Physique et Microphysique* (1947), English trans. in Harper Torchbook 514; A. S. Eddington, *The Nature of the Physical World* (New York, Macmillan, 1928); Id., *The Philosophy of Physical Science* (Cambridge University Press, 1939); W. Heisenberg, *Physics and Philosophy* (New York, Harper, 1958); J. J. Jeans, *The New Background of Science* (New York, Macmillan, 1934); Id., *Physics and Philosophy* (New York, Macmillan, 1945); P. Jordan, *Physics of the 20th Century*, trans. by E. Oshry (New York, Philosophical Library, 1941).

2. *Two Treatises on Government* (1690), *Works*, vol. v (London, 1812).

3. W. Heitler, *Man and Science* (New York, Basic Books, 1963) p. 43.

4. *The Nature of the Physical World*, p. 308.

5. *Physics and Philosophy*, p. 158.

6. So far it has been almost exclusively physicists who have seen the importance of the new science for biology. The vast majority of biologists have shown little interest in this field. The first and most eloquent disciple of Bohr was the atomic physicist Pascual Jordan, who elaborated Bohr's theory in two books: *Anschauliche Quantentheorie* (Berlin, Springer, 1936) and *Die Physik und das Geheimnis des organischen Lebens* (Braunschweig, Vieweg, 1941). The book of another theoretical physicist, W. Heitler (Note 3 above), devotes at least a chapter to biology but treats of the impact of the new physics on man in a general philosophical way. Still another theoretical physicist, W. M. Elsasser, presents an interesting development on the foundation of Bohr in *Atom and Organism* (Princeton University Press, 1966). He differs from Bohr in that he would confine the concept of complementarity to quantum physics and cell biology. It seems to me that, if complementarity begins with space and time (see below), it is more fundamental than quantum physics and more universal than cell biology. In fact, it must be as universal as space and time.

7. W. Heitler, *op. cit.*, p. 43.

8. *Licht und Leben* (1933), *Die Naturwissenschaften*, vol. xxi, p. 245ff.

CHAPTER 2

1. E. Schrödinger, *What Is Life?* (New York, Macmillan, 1946) p. 60.

2. *Op. cit.* (1928), p. 236.

3. Dover Publications, New York, 1953.

4. Oparin, *op. cit.*, Chpt. 5. See also, C. Ponnamperuma and R. Mack, *Science*, vol. 148, no. 3674, p. 1221ff.

5. Cf. S. Alexander, *Space, Time and Deity*, vol. ii, p. 38ff (London, Macmillan, 1927): "Time . . . is the mind of Space and Space the body of Time. . . . Space and Time are . . . not two things but one, and there is no Space without Time nor Time without Space."

6. So far, biologists have rarely used the term "complementarity." Its adoption would lead to greater unification of theoretical biology. The molecular biology of the cell offers hundreds of examples. The synthesis of proteins from nucleic acids is but the progressive complication of complementary compounds. The genetic superiority of heterozygosity over homozygosity (asymmetry over symmetry) seems to rest on the superiority of complementary over mechanical organization. Homeostasis is nothing but the complementary interdependence of all chemical processes within the organism; etc., etc.

7. *Essays*, B. Atkinson, ed. (New York, Modern Library) p. 52.

8. *The Biology of the Spirit* (New York, Viking Compass Books) pp. 64–67, 88.

9. E. W. Sinnott, *op. cit.*; R. S. Lillie, *General Biology and Philosophy of Organism* (Chicago University Press, 1945); B. Rensch, *Homo Sapiens* (Göttingen, 1965).

10. *The Nature of Physical Reality* (New York, McGraw-Hill, 1950).

11. This should not be regarded as one of the traditional "proofs" of the existence of God. For it follows from the nature of complementarity that the more emphatic we can be about our own consciousness, the less certainty we can have concerning the deity. And it would further seem to follow that the more positive and detailed men try to be concerning God, His will and plans, the more they addle their own brains. On the other hand, as we shall see later, the purely ethical content of religion remains intact.

12. *Anschauliche Quantentheorie* (Berlin, 1936) pp. 301–302.

CHAPTER 3

1. The nonbiologist will find a good survey of the problems here involved in Wells-Huxley-Wells, *The Science of Life* (New York, Literary Guild, 1929) Bk. V, Chpts. 4 and 5; Bk. VI, Chpts. 1–3.
2. C. Sherrington, *Man on His Nature* (Cambridge University Press, 1940).
3. "The Biological Basis of Imagination," *Scientific Monthly* (June 1946).
4. *The Grand Strategy of Evolution* (Boston, Badger, 1920) p. 90.
5. Cf. also, C. Sherrington, *op. cit.*, p. 387: "The multicellular organism stood for a change, in so far, from conflict between cell and cell to harmony between cell and cell. Its coming was, we know now, pregnant with an immense advance for the whole future of life upon the globe."
6. *The Brain and its Environment* (New Haven, Yale University Press, 1938).
7. W. Cannon, *The Wisdom of the Body* (New York, Norton, 1938).

CHAPTER 4

1. J. von Uexküll, *Theoretische Biologie*, 2. Aufl. (Berlin, 1928).
2. *Op. cit.*, pp. 119, 140.
3. N. Tinbergen, *Social Releasers and the Experimental Methods Required for their Study* (Ann Arbor, Mich., The Wilson Bulletin, March 1948); similarly, Uexküll, *op. cit.*, p. 121.
4. *Op. cit.*, p. 200.
5. W. Köhler, *The Mentality of Apes* (London, Kegan Paul, 1925).
6. *Vom Ursprung und von den Grenzen der Freiheit* (Basel, 1945).
7. K. Lorenz, *Ueber tierisches und menschliches Verhalten* (München, 1966) vol. i, p. 170; also Bally, *op. cit.*, p. 46ff.

CHAPTER 5

1. Th. Dobzhansky, *The Biological Basis of Human Freedom* (New York, Columbia University Press, 1956) p. 28.

2. *The Leviathan* (1651). W. G. P. Smith, ed. (Oxford, Clarendon Press, 1943).

3. G. W. F. Hegel, *The Philosophy of History*, trans. by J. Sibree (New York, Dover, 1956) e.g., pp. 19, 456.

4. Quoted by C. Wissler, *An Introduction to Social Anthropology* (New York, Holt, 1920).

5. Quoted by E. Kahler, *Man the Measure* (New York, Pantheon Books, 1943) p. 33.

6. *Ibid.*, p. 33.

7. See Fustel de Coulanges, *La cité antique*, 10th ed. (Paris, 1833).

8. Deut. 28, 58–61.

9. *The Laws of Manu*, trans. by C. Bühler (Oxford, Clarendon, 1886).

10. *Anthropologie der Naturvölker*, vol. 1 (Leipzig, 1859).

11. Death penalty may be imposed, e.g., for the mention of the name of a brother-in-law or of a dead person. See G. Frazer, *The Golden Bough* (New York, Macmillan, 1958) pp. 292, 297.

12. G. E. Coghill, *Anatomy and the Problem of Behaviour* (Cambridge University Press, 1929) pp. 91ff.

CHAPTER 6

1. "The Ant Colony as an Organism," *Journ. of Morphol.*, vol. 22, pp. 307–325.

2. For a review of this subject, see E. O. Wilson, "Chemical Communication in the Social Insects," *Science*, 149, no. 3688 (1965).

3. *The Nature of the Physical World*, p. 276.

4. *Bees, Their Vision, Chemical Senses and Languages* (Ithaca, N. Y., Cornell University Press, 1950).

5. A. Portmann, *Biologische Fragmente zu einer Lehre vom Menschen* (Basel, 1944) pp. 51–69.

6. *The Phenomenon of Man* (New York, Harper, 1959).

7. A. Jolly mentions the disruption of the social order of the lemurs during the mating season. *Science*, vol. 153, no. 3735 (1966).

8. Quoted by L. L. Whyte, *The Unitary Principle in Physics and Biology* (New York, Holt, 1949). Concerning the important

differences between symmetry and asymmetry, see also Eddington, *op. cit.* (1928) p. 236.

9. *Vom Ursprung und von den Grenzen der Freiheit* (Basel, 1945).

10. *The Biological Basis of Human Freedom*, p. 131.

11. K. Lorenz, *On Aggression* (New York, Harcourt, 1966).

12. *Op. cit.* (1956) p. 27. Also his *Mankind Evolving* (New Haven, Yale University Press, 1962) Chpts. 1–4, 12.

CHAPTER 7

1. This was already stressed by the poet Schiller. *Ueber die ästhetische Erziehung des Menschen*, 14. Brief (1794). Meyers Klassiker Ausgaben, 8. Bd.

2. *Op. cit.*, 15. Brief.

3. *The Greek Way to Western Civilization* (New York, Norton, 1948) and Mentor Books, No. 32, p. 16.

CHAPTER 8

1. L. Robbins, ed. (London, Routledge, 1935).

2. New York, Oxford University Press, vol. iii. See his Index under "Militarism."

CHAPTER 9

1. See also, Bally, *op. cit.* (note 9, ch. 6), pp. 105–113.

2. *Process and Reality* (New York, Columbia University Press, 1944).

3. *Ueber die ästhetische Erziehung des Menschen*, 25. Brief.

4. *The Wisdom of Confucius*, Lin Yutang, ed. (New York, Modern Library, 1938) pp. 218–219.

5. Matt. 10, 35–36.

6. *A Study of History*, vol. ii, p. 97.

7. "The moral man finds the moral law beginning in the relations between man and woman, but ending in the vast reaches of the universe." Confucius, *op. cit.*, p. 108.

CHAPTER 10

1. Harvard University Press, 1963.

2. My wife informs me that all this is evident also from the oldest Chinese pictograph (ca. 1800 B.C.) for *chün*, prince. It represents a human figure with horned headgear, exaggerated arms and open mouth. Horns and arms symbolize brute power, the open mouth dictatorial law. Here too, then, there is *Imponiergehaben*.

3. *Das Mutterrecht* (Stuttgart, 1862).

4. See also E. Bergmann, *Erkenntnisgeist und Muttergeist*, 2. Aufl. (Breslau, 1933); R. H. Lowie, *The Matriarchal Complex*, University of California Publications in American Archeology and Ethnology, vol. 16, No. 2 (1919); R. Briffault, *The Mothers* (New York, Macmillan, 1931)—The Matriarchal Theory is generally rejected by orthodox sociology. This is justified insofar as it contains political elements. But if we recognize that the matriarchal phase was "purely social," it becomes an important and necessary transitional stage between the mammalian family and political civilization.

5. R. H. Lowie, *Primitive Society* (New York, Boni & Liveright, 1920).

6. To matriarchal primitivity the idea of a Savior was unknown. As an essentially biological world it was complete in itself, balanced, if stagnant. In the new order of masculine dominance, from the beginning "a world out of joint," it became a necessity. The male created the "mysticism of salvation . . . in the same basic form among all peoples, all civilizations. Knowledge, proclamation of the dogma, martyrdom, atonement, death, resurrection," these are the stages of practically all doctrines of salvation. E. Bergmann, *op. cit.*, p. 167ff.

CHAPTER 11

1. According to the missionary Dobrizhoffer, a Paraguay Indian tribe still officially recognizes women as the creators of language. Their religious beliefs prohibit mention of the name of a dead person. Since personal names are usually taken from animals, plants and other common objects, each of these must be given a new name after the death of a person called after them. The invention of new words is the business of the old squaws and their new coinages are adopted by the whole tribe with amazing promptness and with-

out opposition. J. G. Frazer, *The Golden Bough* (New York, Macmillan, 1958) pp. 296–7.

2. We leave undecided the question whether other "primitives" with male dominance represent civilizations arrested as soon as begun or survivors of a condition preceding matriarchy. Among apes, both male and female leadership are found. It is not impossible that in the course of primate history the pendulum swung a number of times from one side to the other.

3. *Eranos-Jahrbuch* XVIII (Sonderband für C. G. Jung, Rhein-Verlag, Zürich, 1950) p. 327.

4. J. H. Breasted, A *History of Egypt*, 2nd ed., 1948 reissue (New York, Scribner); A. Toynbee, *op. cit.*, vol. 1, pp. 137, 141f, 302ff.

5. Breasted, *op. cit.*, p. 86.

6. Aristotle, *Politics*, 1269b ff.

CHAPTER 12

1. In a modified form the tradition survives in the Roman Catholic Church as canonization.

2. J. K. Galbraith, *The Affluent Society* (Boston, Houghton Mifflin, 1958) deals with many aspects of this problem under the heading "the conventional wisdom." "It is never in such peril as when enthusiastic exponents put it to a practical test."

3. *Modern Democracies* (New York, Macmillan, 1921) vol. i, p. 70ff.

4. In New York I personally knew (besides others of an ampler caliber) two college professors, one a full professor, whom I could classify only as palliated primitives. They had learned to read, had middling memories, but nary a thought of their own. The full professor could not even think up examination questions; he had to copy them out of textbooks.

5. See A. A. Berle, *Power Without Property* (New York, Harcourt, 1959).

6. The view of a biologist of genius is worth quoting in this connection: "It would seem that *homo praedatorius* is in a backwater unreached by the tide which set in millennia since. . . . The ascendency of *homo praedatorius* would spell ruin to man's prosperous leadership here. And man must lead or go. . . . But leadership does not lie in treating as prey those it leads. Man is above all a

leader charged with the survival of the 'values' which are in his keeping. Man's leadership cannot be tyranny since that would be to forget the 'values.'" Sir Charles Sherrington, *Man on His Nature*, p. 396.

7. What I say in this section has, incidentally, the approval of my wife, who spent most of her life in the academic world.

CHAPTER 13

1. J. G. Herder, *Ideen zur Philosophie der Geschichte der Menschheit* (1784–1791), 15. Buch, v, 1, and 13. Buch vii.

2. G. W. F. Hegel, *Philosophy of History* (ca. 1825), trans. by Sibree (New York, Dover, 1956).

3. *The Positive Philosophy of Auguste Comte* (1851–1854), trans. by H. Martineau, 2 vols. (London, 1893).

4. Cf. Emerson's scathing words, "Every actual State is corrupt. . . . What satire on government can equal the severity of censure conveyed in the word *politic*, which now for ages has signified *cunning*, intimating that the State is a trick." *Essays* (New York, Modern Library, 1940) p. 427.

5. Articles I, III, V, and VI of the Bill of Rights offer specific instances as to how the "due process" is to be observed.

6. J. J. Kindt-Kiefer, *Ueber die Fundamentalstruktur des Staates* (Bern, 1940), p. 193.

7. D. Schindler, *Verfassungsrecht und soziale Struktur* (Zürich, 1932).

8. *The Meaning of Evolution* (New Haven, Yale University Press, 1949) p. 281.

9. "Individualization is a means of socialization and socialization provides enriched opportunities for individualization." G. G. Simpson, *op. cit.*, p. 317.

CHAPTER 14

1. G. G. Simpson, *The Meaning of Evolution*, p. 233f.

2. *Das Problem der Menschwerdung* (Jena, G. Fischer, 1925).

3. Martin Buber, *Ich und Du* (1923), 1958 ed. (Heidelberg, Lambert Schneider) pp. 26–29.

4. A famous physicist said: "And I for my part do not believe that these eternal laws are limited to the physical world either." R. A. Millikan, in *Human Biology and Social Welfare*, E. V. Cowdry, ed. (New York, Hoeber, 1930).

CHAPTER 15

1. D. Schindler, in *Werdende Rechte* (Tübingen, Festgabe für Fritz Fleiner, 1927) p. 402.

2. An example is the preponderance of lawyers in all legislatures, which amounts to a gross form of misrepresentation.

3. *The National Observer*, June 3, 1963.

4. The problem is as old as history. Cf. Kant, *Kritik der reinen Vernunft* (1781) Hartenstein ed., p. 249: "It is an ancient wish, which may yet, however late, reach fulfilment, that some day men may, instead of the infinite manifoldness of the civil laws, search for their principles; for therein alone can rest the secret of the simplification of legislation, as it is called."

5. See H. Friedmann, *Die Welt der Formen* (München, Beck, 1932) p. 252: to no thoughtful observer can it be hidden "that the simplicity of this [deterministic] mode of thought is surpassed only by its insufficiency"; also, W. M. Elsasser, *Atom and Organism* (Princeton University Press, 1966) pp. 105–106, 108.

6. By "science" I do not of course mean its bastards known as "scientism" and "technocracy." These are infantile pipe dreams of a sort of better shop mechanics still living in the nineteenth century.

7. The first sputnik has somewhat altered the situation, but only as regards the military and medical importance of science.

CHAPTER 16

1. N. S. Timasheff, *An Introduction to the Sociology of Law* (Cambridge, Mass., Harvard Sociological Studies, 1939) vol. iii, p. 282.

2. New York, Harcourt Brace, 1959, Harvest Book Edition, pp. 77–79.

3. Actually, the beginnings of such an ethic are to be found in some free medieval cities of Europe, where the craft guilds wrenched dominance from the patrician merchants. The guilds maintained high standards of production, fixed prices at moderate levels, thus

also protecting the customers. They evolved the first civic ethic in history. Most of these gains were lost when, with the age of discoveries, capitalism rose to power. —A few of the recent books on ethics may be mentioned here: C. H. Waddington's (a biologist) *The Ethical Animal* (New York, Atheneum, 1961) contains many references to the works of other scientists touching on the subject, but maintains the traditional attitude and treats ethic as a person-to-person affair; Bertrand Russell's (mathematician and philosopher) *Human Society in Ethics and Politics* (New York, Simon & Schuster, 1955) devotes thirteen chapters to private ethics, often somewhat sarcastically, and five chapters to politics. Characteristically, Russell hopes to improve politics by intelligence alone. All ethic would seem to appear atavistic to him; A. A. Berle's (a legal scholar) *Power Without Property* (see Note 2) shows understanding for the connections of ethic, business and politics. The little volume of two journalists, M. W. Childs and D. Cater, *Ethics in a Business Society* (New York, Harper, 1954) summarizes a series of sociological studies organized by the National Council of the Churches of Christ and financed by the Rockefeller Foundation. Here one finds the clearest indications of a religiously motivated trend which the present study found imperative on evolutionary grounds.

4. Cf. E. Durkheim, *On the Division of Labor in Society* (New York, Macmillan, 1933): "Because there are now more ways of acquiring property, there are also more ways of stealing."

5. See, e.g., A. Wenzel, *Einstein's Theory of Relativity, etc.*, in *Albert Einstein, Philosopher–Scientist*, P. A. Schilpp ed. (New York, Harper Torch Books, 1959) vol. ii, pp. 583–606.

6. *The Nature of the Physical World*, pp. 295, 344.

7. *Republic* v, 473, trans. by Jowett (New York, Random House, 1939), vol. i, p. 737.

8. *A Study of History* (New York, Oxford, 1939), vol. vi, pp. 242–259.

9. E.g., *Geist und Materie* (Braunschweig, 1961); also, W. Heisenberg, *Science and Philosophy* (New York, Harper, 1958) Chpt. xi; P. Jordan, *Die Physik und das Geheimnis des organischen Lebens* (Braunschweig, 1941), says: ". . . nobody will be able to remove out of the world the fact that through these new insights [of modern physics] the great old problems of a centuries-filling struggle between science and religion have *come to the fore again*" (p. 168).

10. *The Biology of the Spirit* (1955; New York, Viking, 1961); *Matter, Mind and Man* (1957; New York, Atheneum, 1962); *The Bridge of Life* (New York, Simon & Schuster, 1966) —If scientists find that they can no longer discuss their greatest problems without reference to religion, theologians and churches have proved themselves less broadminded (there are, to be sure, blinkered scientists too). The danger of stagnant religions has been touched upon in Chapter 12. If our present churches remain untouched by the spirit of science, they too may become as anachronistic and parasitic as tapeworms.

11. W. Heitler, *Man and Science* (New York, Basic Books, 1963) p. 28. See also, C. Sherrington, *Man on His Nature*, 2nd ed. (Cambridge University Press, 1963) Chpt. xi.

CHAPTER 17

1. P. W. Bridgman, *The Nature of Physical Theory* (1936; New York, Dover, n.d.) p. 131.

2. The mind has of course more than two aspects, but complementary pairs within the greater manifold are more conspicuous than the psychic entity. We find complementary pairs even in very specialized mental domains. All scientists could, e.g., be classified either as the visionary or intuitive type, concerned mainly with theoretico-morphological problems, and the more purely technical type. A related division holds for the arts, and not seldom we find eminent contemporary representatives of both types, giving us such pairs as Raphael and Michelangelo, Handel and Bach, Mozart and Beethoven (none of them a pure type, though).

3. P. W. Bridgman, *op. cit.*, p. 123. The calculus of probability defines the laws of chance.

4. See, e.g., Bertrand Russell, *Authority and the Individual* (New York, Simon & Schuster, 1949), p. 74: "To believe that there can be good or evil in a collection of human beings, over and above the good or evil in the various individuals, is an error." This may follow from the abstract rational logic of the schools, at which Russell excels; it does not follow from evolutionary logic, which is irrational.

5. P. Teilhard de Chardin, *The Phenomenon of Man* (New York, Harper, 1959). In seeing humanity, or the state, as a mere collective, such birds of different feather as Teilhard de Chardin and Bertrand Russell weirdly agree, because neither thinks organically.

Index

(The colon between two words indicates a complementary relationship)

293

Dynamics, 30, 36
see also Statics

E

Economy, 96, 108, 130, 221,
226–231, 237, 248, 258
limitations of, 115–122
natural, 230
Eddington, A. S., 18, 86, 253
his "great point of bifurcation," 31f., 103, 122, 125
Education, 177f., 271
Egalitarianism, 33, 45, 121, 175,
176, 192, 213
Egg cell, 22
Ego, Egoism, 134, 215, 237
see also Individual, Individualism
Egypt, 79, 165–167, 172, 175,
180, 182, 184
Einstein, A., 20, 141, 207, 239
Electricity, 21, 22
Electron, 22, 26, 36
Electronic-dynamic phenomena,
87, 146
Emergents, 39, 89
Emerson, R. W., 40, 285
Environment, 39–42, 48–50, 57,
63, 76, 151, 152, 164
social, 43–46, 89–102, 160–161
see also Organism : Environ-
ment, Adaptation
Equality, 177
see also Egalitarianism, Freedom
Eskimos, 76, 77
Ethics, Ethos, 7, 83, 91, 96, 97,
98, 103, 116, 121f., 130–140,
149, 164, 193, 197, 204, 220,

237, 238, 242–249, 251, 253,
255ff., 263, 266, 269, 270,
272, 273
in civilization, 245–247
a manifestation of complementarity, 98, 244
Evolution, 5, 24, 59, 60, 61, 70,
79, 80, 87, 96, 110, 121, 122,
127f., 134, 145, 146, 208,
212, 214, 243, 244, 252, 263,
269
as development of comple-
mentarity, 21, 23f.
social, 43, 44, 59, 61, 81, 100,
102, 105, 108, 122, 133,
136, 147, 187, 218, 220, 241
political, 44, 136–140, 147–
154, 191, 205, 216, 232, 237,
240, 241
"horizontal," 146
"vertical," 146

F

Family, 89, 90, 92, 94, 104, 109,
110, 170, 187
Feedbacks, 37, 92
Female, 93, 144–146, 149, 180
see also Dominance, Matriarchy, Sex, Woman
Feudalism, 175, 179, 182, 240,
248
economic, 228, 240
Food Instinct, 60, 62, 65, 68,
94–97, 105, 109, 133, 221
the basis of economy, 115
Freedom, 2, 4, 5, 7, 15, 17–19,
30, 33f., 41, 45, 70, 80, 106,
109, 110, 138, 183, 195, 222,
241–263, 274